In Code

In Code

A Mathematical Journey

Sarah Flannery

with David Flannery

PROFILE BOOKS

First published in 2000 by

Profile Books Ltd
58A Hatton Garden
London EC1N 8LX
www.profilebooks.co.uk

Typeset in Times by
macguru2@appleonline.net

Printed and bound in Great Britain by
St Edmundsbury Press, Bury St Edmunds

A CIP catalogue record for this book is available from the British Library.

ISBN 1 86197 222 9

Acknowledgements for the photographs that appear in the book are as follows:
Eddie O'Hare 1, 2, 9, 13, 14
Newspics 3, 5
Bryan Murphy 7
Sygma 8
All others are from the Flannery family albums.

Contents

Preface   ix

1   Early Influences   1
2   Mathematical Excursions   26
3   What Matters Is What's Left Over   61
4   Sums with a Difference   102
5   One Way Only   136
6   Exhibition Time   166
7   After-math   199

About This Book   234
Appendix A   Solution to Puzzles   236
Appendix B   Answers to Miscellaneous Questions   239
Appendix C   Euclid's Algorithm   247
Appendix D   The Euler ϕ-function and the
               Euler–Fermat Theorem   257

Acknowledgements   263
Bibliography   265
Index   267

To Michael Purser and William Whyte

Preface

*E*arly on the morning of Wednesday 6 January 1999 our sixteen-year-old daughter Sarah set off from the village of Blarney for Dublin in the company of her science teacher Seán Foley and his son Vincent. Their destination was the Royal Dublin Society building in Ballsbridge, where Sarah and Vincent were to submit individual projects in the Physics, Chemistry and Mathematics category for the annual Esat Telecom Young Scientist Competition. The following Friday, watching the televised award ceremony at home, I was to witness with delight Vincent's winning of the prestigious Intel Award for Excellence in Science followed by Sarah's being declared by the Taoiseach Bertie Ahern the competition's overall winner and Ireland's Young Scientist of the Year 1999. Her award was a magnificent silver trophy, IR£1000 and a one-week trip to Thessaloniki, Greece, to represent Ireland at the European Contest for Young Scientists in September.

Sarah's winning project, entitled 'Cryptography – A New Algorithm Versus the RSA', dealt with the science of secrecy. It was given high praise by one of the competition judges during a television interview that same evening. On being asked if the project had any commercial potential, he answered, "If she plays her cards right I think she should make a lot of money ... ". The following day one Irish newspaper headline read JUDGES BAFFLED BY YOUNG GENIUS. Needless to say, whether or not any of these statements could withstand close scrutiny, the 'lots of money/genius' combination made an irresistibly attractive story for the press at large. World media attention was ensured when an article, not differing much in content from some of those that had already appeared in the Irish papers, and intended for modest inclusion somewhere in the inside pages of the London *Times*, was front-paged at the last moment. The feature was accompanied by a picture of Sarah in front of a blackboard which was covered by an array of mathematical symbols scribbled by her to please a photographer. Beneath what she regarded as this awful picture was the caption "Sarah Flannery, 16, who baffled the judges with her grasp of cryptography. They described her work as 'brilliant'". This article sparked off an explosion of worldwide interest in a young girl who a week before was leading the life of a normal sixteen-year-old.

One consequence of this article was an invitation from Profile Books to both Sarah and me (as her father and mathematical mentor, who allegedly cultivated her interest in mathematics) to write a book telling a little of her life up to the winning of the award and to recount some of the events that unfolded in the months that followed. Although the book is written in the first person (Sarah), I helped to write the mathematical sections so that she could continue, as best she could, with her schoolwork. For her mother and me, her achievement is not that she became famous for a brief period of time but that she had the interest and courage to undertake what she did. At her age I would not have been brave enough to talk with confidence to experts had I trodden but the narrowest of paths through the mathematical landscape.

David Flannery
January 2000

Preface

"Do I need to know mathematics to read this book?"

Not at all! If mathematics is not for you, we suggest that you just skim Chapters 3 and 4 to acquaint yourself with the little terminology and notation that is used sparingly in later chapters. We hope that the personal narrative in the rest of the book will interest you.

However, should you relish a challenge and can add, subtract, multiply, divide and raise a number to a power (e.g. $3^3 = 27$), and you know what a square root is, then you might wish to learn, in a pleasant way, the very little extra mathematics that breathes life into the story. You will be well rewarded by acquiring an understanding of what is, at bottom, not difficult mathematics.

Those two chapters were written in an attempt to have the book self-contained, something which we realise is probably overly ambitious. But more importantly, perhaps, they are included for the many readers of popular scientific books who, once their interest has been sparked by the subject matter, often wish there was just a little more of mathematical substance.

Anyone reading new ideas must occasionally reread a line or paragraph to recall points which may be forgotten or to clarify those which were not entirely obvious first time round. Do take this trouble when the need arises, and don't despair even if a rereading doesn't immediately do the trick. Keep going – without necessarily understanding every detail or fathoming the notation, you'll be surprised how much of the overall picture you will still absorb by simply forging ahead.

Sarah and David Flannery
January 2000

1. Early Influences

*T*here is a blackboard in our kitchen. It might be said that my mathematical journey began there. But before I tell you how I got interested in mathematics I would like to say a little about who I am. I'll just give a few basic details – by the end of this book I fear you may know more of my character than perhaps I wished to reveal. I would also like to tell you a little about my closest relations, who had the greatest influence on me while I was growing up.

I am the eldest of five children and live with my parents and four younger brothers, "the boys", in an old house in the middle of a farm two kilometres from the village of Blarney, County Cork. We have only one neighbour, the farm owner who lives with his family a few hundred metres away. I attend the village's co-educational secondary school, Scoil Mhuire gan Smál. I received my primary education at the local all-girls school, and so have grown up with much the same people all my life. Other than the mathematics that this book describes, my main interests are athletics, showjumping, basketball, Gaelic football and hurling, reading, playing the piano and listening to lots of different types of music.

Both my parents are very independent-minded people. They rarely express political opinions on a party basis and are pretty much apolitical. However, they take referenda very seriously and joke about being seldom on the winning side. They have taught us to respect the culture and beliefs of all people and to value objective truth very highly. They advise us to be ourselves and to rate moral courage above all other forms. They insist that we speak distinctly and slowly – which is a virtual impossibility for anybody immersed in the rich, fast-flowing Blarney brogue. Perhaps there is, after all, some truth in the legend of the Blarney Stone, which is said to bestow the 'gift of the gab' on all those who kiss it. Thousands of visitors come to perform this ritual each year, making our small village one of Ireland's most popular tourist destinations. I'd like to kiss it too, but I'm told that I talk enough as it is! I may be deluding myself, but I believe that both Mom and Dad are regarded as private but friendly people.

My mother claims that she had a wonderful childhood growing up on the family farm. She's a bit of a tomboy (she won't mind my saying so) probably because, being the eldest of nine children, she had to assume the role of eldest son with all its traditional duties. This meant that from an early age she milked cows, mucked out, stacked and stored hay bales, picked stones and best of all was allowed to use the farm machinery to plough, rotavate, harrow, mow, and harvest silage and grain. How I envy her freedom to do all this, I who must satisfy all sorts of legal and other requirements just to drive a boring old car. She's hard pressed to find use for her varied farm skills now that we only have a garden but she still prefers to be outdoors. She left home at eighteen for university, where she studied microbiology, a subject about which she is most passionate. She lectures part-time at the same institute as Dad – the Cork Institute of Technology (CIT), eight kilometres away. She is very cool and has a calming influence on us all. She loves writing limericks, mostly about my father's idiosyncrasies – he appears not to mind being the butt of these well crafted lines. At night-time she likes to take out her guitar and sing. She has a fine voice, and whenever I see her and my brother Michael playing guitar and singing together I make sure Dad knows how much I hate him for the fact that I have inherited his crow-like voice. They like to harmonise and of late are doing songs from Bob Dylan's *Desire* album.

My father's passion is mathematics, so he spends a lot of time in the sitting room 'studying'. His enthusiasm must rub off because

Mom has told me of the many times she has been cornered by a student wishing to let her know what a great lecturer they think Dad is, and how "he makes maths come alive". He is not a sporty type, either of the television-viewing or go-out-and-do-it variety, but he played poker for years to bring in extra income. He loved chess as a student and has taught all of us how to play, but we much prefer outdoor sports. He has a few devoted friends, mostly intellectual types with liberal views. He hates socialising in the 'come to dinner' style, which is a pity as my mother is very fond of people and civilised ways. However, he can spend hours talking in a pub, particularly with his brothers, who relish verbal sparring on any issue, good, bad or indifferent. I really enjoy listening to these conversations in the grown-up atmosphere.

My brother Michael lives for the day when he can deliver a knock-out piece of repartee to his Uncle Paul, a barrister much given to biting sarcasm but who admits freely that it is only a matter of time before we younger ones gain the upper hand. This good-humoured uncle once said to me in frustration, "Would you ever go away and develop a few complexes." Dad thought this was hilarious and a high compliment to me.

My mother's father is the most independent-minded man one is ever likely to encounter and a legend in his own community as a 'genius with machinery'. This is undisputed: for example, when he needed a more powerful tractor but couldn't afford it, he made one. He bought a lorry engine and completely modified his Fordson Major tractor to make the new engine fit. My mother says that she remembers people coming from miles around to watch this undertaking and to try out the finished product on nearby Barleymount Hill, a steep incline which forces all vehicles down through their gears but which made no impression on the new Major as it soared up in top gear. He is largely a self-educated man who came, after much thought, to be an avowed atheist at a time when it was uncomfortable and unwise to be open about being one in a small, predominantly Catholic farming community. My father, an agnostic, teases him that by expressing himself with such certainty he is being as dogmatic as any of the old-style priests he so criticised, but my grandfather replies that agnostics are wimps who are afraid to face the obvious. My father and my grandfather get on very well together because they value 'things of the mind' but never take themselves too seriously. My grandfather has a passion for astronomy and a fascination for everything that is either 'the biggest' or 'the longest' or 'the strongest' ... but has no interest in the 'smallest', and is totally incapable of making small talk. He will bring any conversation, no matter how varied its participants, around to one of his pet topics in no time at all and will insist on getting their opinions on the most erudite of matters whether they are interested or not. He loves animals and is a pacifist.

My maternal grandmother must be a saint, having lived with an other-worldly obsessive all her life while trying to raise their nine children. She loves traditional Irish music and set dancing, and is the stereotypical welcoming and generous farm-wife who never lets anyone out her door without first having tea and her famous soda bread. She has made many a witty remark to put my grandfather in his place. On one occasion, after he had told a visitor how much he would like to live in a Mediterranean climate and enthused about the siesta custom ("I'd love that – a sleep in the middle of the day") my grandmother peeped round the door and chided him with, "You wouldn't be up in time!" (He stays up so late on winter nights watching the stars or reading about them that he is not always an early riser.)

My paternal grandfather began life as a railway clerk at seventeen, paying more in rent than he was earning, and retired as one of the chief executives of the company forty-three years later. He and his father before him loved mathematics and were noted for their natural ability at it. My great-grandfather was always being called upon to 'step out' land for the purpose of ascertaining its area. My grandfather says that his father's brother, known as 'Yellow Jack' because of his jaundiced complexion, was regarded as an even better mathematician. These men, with no more than primary education, were not mathematicians in the modern sense but they were gifted calculators and knew some geometry. My grandfather scored 99, 97 and 100 per cent, respectively, in arithmetic, algebra and geometry for his Intermediate Certificate at a time when these exams, he would have us believe, were much harder. I remember him telling me of how he saw a mason using strings of lengths 3, 4 and 5 to form a right-angled triangle which he said was a practical use of the converse of Pythagoras' theorem. He loves puzzles of all types. He always did the *Irish Times* Simplex crossword but when he retired he set about learning how to do the cryptic version – the Crosaire. He mastered this art in a few weeks after many exasperating efforts, tenaciously examining the published solutions on the following day. Now he instructs my mother in how to decipher their mysteries, which my father, who refuses even to try them, describes as the outpourings of a warped mind.

Married for soon-to-be fifty years, he and Grandma had eight children of whom my father is the eldest. I know that most women of her generation stayed at home to rear the children, but Grandma sacrificed more than her own career to support Grandad in his. Time and again, due to his promotions in the company, she had to pack her bags, uproot her children, say goodbye to neighbours and friends and move to a different town, setting up house no less than ten times. She is noted for a deep intuition about people and is rarely found wanting in her assessments. She is an extremely efficient housekeeper, often preparing four-course dinners for as many as fourteen without apparent effort. Everybody else gets to do the washing-up. I often marvel at her boundless energy and zest for life. Since Grandad retired, she and he seem to be as often on holiday as they are at home. They are both avid card players and are formidable bridge partners, playing several nights a week. Dad says jokingly that his parents unwittingly steered him towards single-person games such as chess and poker where you have nobody to blame but yourself. None of us knows how to play bridge though my grandparents are always threatening to put things right in that respect, despite whatever reservations any of us might have.

I didn't get any special tuition in mathematics while I was growing up. I was left to my own devices. I could and did ask for help now and then with homework, and I still do. My brothers are also free to seek help with their exercises from my parents, though it is suspected that some of them would rather die than receive such assistance. The reason for this is simple: you often get more help than you want. You run the risk of a little homily on how nice a poem is or "Isn't it very clever how that is done", when all you want is the question answered quickly so you can get your homework out of the way and be free!

Strictly speaking, it is not true to say that I or my brothers don't get any help with mathematics. We are given no extra classes, nor do we have to endure intense sessions at the kitchen table from over-zealous parents. But almost without our knowing we have been receiving help since we were very young, out-of-the-ordinary help of a subtle and playful kind which I think has made us self-confident in problem-solving. Ever since I can remember, my father has set us little problems and puzzles. How often have I heard, and still hear, "Dad, give us a puzzle." These puzzles were challenging and encouraged curiosity, and many of them made maths interesting and tangible. More fundamentally, they taught us how to reason and think for ourselves. It is in this way that puzzles have been far more beneficial to me than years of learning formulae and 'proofs'.

I hope now, with the use of a few model puzzles, to show some of the many lessons I learned. The puzzles are not too difficult, and answers are provided to illustrate the points I wish to make. Before skipping to the solutions, however, do try your best to solve them. The solutions to those puzzles which are not discussed further can be found in Appendix A.

Many puzzles are simply numerical in nature, as is the one that follows. I was given it at a young age, probably when I was about five years old. It crops up in the film *Die Hard with a Vengeance*. The inept attempts of the characters played by Bruce Willis and Samuel Jackson at a solution had one of my brothers nearly on top of the TV trying to communicate the answer.

The Two Jars Puzzle: *Given a five litre jar and a three litre jar and an unlimited supply of water, how do you measure out four litres exactly?*

Early Influences

Bear in mind that we, my brothers and I, are given puzzles under less harrowing conditions than those in the film, and whether or not we solve them is not for us a matter of life or death. At times, though, you would be forgiven for thinking that this is so. You'll often hear a bad-tempered "Be quiet will you, I'm thinking!" hurled by one of the younger family members at an older one who is acting all superior and is teasing, "That's simple" or "That's too hard for you, dumbo." Needless to say, the arrogant older brother has heard the puzzle before and knows (or is it remembers?) the answer. To put him in his box he'll be given a right twister.

Dad likes to make the most of a simple puzzle by extending it a little whenever possible. For example, when you solve this two jar problem and are hoping to be rewarded by being given another puzzle of a different type you are more likely to hear, "Now see if you can measure out exactly one litre." This is easy, but when you do it (and presuming you have not become bored) he will then suggest that you try the same problem with nine and four litre jars to get *all* the possible measures between one and thirteen litres. Of course this is a little more taxing, but it gets you beyond trial-and-error to thinking. When eventually you succeed in doing it you are then asked, "How might you do this most efficiently?" At this Mom says, "Mathematicians can never leave well enough alone – what if this, what if that? They take the good out of it. You never get to the end of anything." How true, but it can be great fun. This is perhaps what makes the puzzles so worthwhile: some have the germs of greater things in them. When presented to enthusiastic children hungry for challenges, they can teach them a lot about logical thinking while providing amusement.

When you tire of all this careful water-pouring and think that surely now you deserve a fresh puzzle you might hear, "I'll give you a new puzzle, but first tell me how to measure four litres exactly given only a six litre jar and a three litre jar." "Ahh Dad!" What's worse, after a while you realise that this cannot be done. This variation on a theme lets you learn the very valuable lesson that sometimes problems may not have solutions of the type you seek (and that you cannot trust even your own father to give you solvable puzzles). Sometimes when I am really stuck I'll take a chance with, "I'll bet this is one of your stupid has-no-solution puzzles" but this doesn't always put an end to the agony of not being able to find an answer. I must say, though, that it is a well-tried method of fishing for clues when things get just a little too depressing and you lose your will to keep searching.

Sometimes Dad sets really good puzzles which can have people hopping about the room trying to figure out what could possibly be wrong with their seemingly logical answers while he just sits chuckling at the head of the table. You have to watch for puzzles where the answer that first comes to mind seems just too easy. The following, which is also in the purely numerical vein, should convince you that sometimes $3 - 2 \neq 1$.

The Rabbit Puzzle: *A rabbit falls into a dry well, thirty metres deep. Since to be at the bottom of a well was not in her original scheme of things, she decides to climb out. When she attempts to do so she finds that after going up three metres (and this is the sad bit) she slips back two. Frustrated, she stops where she is for that day and resumes her efforts the following morning – with the same result. How many days does it take her to get out of the well?*

Don't be hasty in leaping to conclusions. Once you *see* and solve (or just hear the solution to) a problem of this type you learn to be careful and watch out for little wrinkles. See if you have learned this lesson by trying the next one.

The One Hundred Metre Race Puzzle: *If A, B and C run a 100 metre race, each running at a uniform speed throughout, and if A beats B by 10 metres and B beats C by 10 metres, by how much does A beat C?*

Whether aided or unaided, you experience a great feeling of self-satisfaction and pride when you finally crack a problem. Recently my nine-year-old brother David was asked, "What is the smallest number with *exactly* seven factors?" This kept him quiet for a while.

Early Influences

In fact, the puzzle was a little too hard for him (or at least it did not spark off much interest) and he appeared to be doing no thinking about it because I heard him ask a day or two later for a different puzzle, only to hear, "But you didn't solve the last one I gave you." Hearing some evasive excuse, Dad, contrary to his usual practice of never giving the least hint, took David to the blackboard in the kitchen and got him to do some calculations. Then he gave him a little nudge in the right direction (factors coming in pairs). Then I heard a most enthusiastic "Oh, yeah", and I saw David's eyes light up. In no time at all he had the answer scribbled on the board, and after confidently finishing off with a full stop he put down the chalk and turned round, smiling like a Cheshire cat. "That was cool", he said as he skipped off to his next pursuit.

Here now is my favourite puzzle. It requires only simple arithmetic, but the thought processes of a detective. I especially like the look that develops on people's faces as I start to tell it – a look which by the end shows that they certainly think I'm cracked. See what you think when you first read it.

The Insurance Man Puzzle: *An insurance salesman knocks on the door of a home in a housing estate. When a lady answers he asks, "How many children do you have?" She replies, "Three." When he asks, "What are their ages?" she decides that he is too cheeky and refuses to tell him. After he apologises for his apparent rudeness he asks for a hint about the children's ages. She says, "If you multiply their three ages you get 36." (Their ages are exact numbers.) He thinks for a while and then asks for another hint. When she says, "The sum of their ages is the number on the house next door", he immediately jumps over the fence to determine this number. This done, he returns to the lady and asks for one last hint. "All right so", she says, "the eldest plays the piano!" He then knows their ages. Do you?*

It really isn't a very difficult problem, but I like it because it is an exercise in methodical or vertical thinking. Study the facts as they are presented, think about them logically and do not be distracted by talk of piano players. I discuss the solution a little further on.

Meanwhile here is a completely different problem requiring no numerical skills but which tests observation and might appeal to those of a literary bent:

The Text Puzzle: *Study this paragraph and all things in it. What is vitally wrong with it? Actually, nothing in it is wrong, but you must admit that it is most unusual. Don't just zip through it quickly but study it scrupulously. With luck you should spot what is so particular about it and all words found in it. Can you say what it is? Tax your brains and try again. Don't miss a word or a symbol. It isn't all that difficult.*

Hint: cryptanalysts (the guys who try to crack cryptosystems – when they work for us we think of them as very clever fellows, but when they work for the enemy we think of them as low-down sneaks) would spot the answer immediately.

Do not read on unless you have tried very hard to solve these puzzles.

Let's begin with the insurance man puzzle. You might reason that one child is aged 2, and another 3, so that the remaining child is 6, since $2 \times 3 \times 6 = 36$. Thus you have found one possible 'triple' $\{2, 3, 6\}$. You might then discover that another solution is $\{2, 2, 9\}$. At this point you'll probably adopt a more systematic approach to finding the possible ages. You could start by asking, "What is the smallest possible age a child can be?" Since we are dealing with exact numbers the answer to this question is 1. Given this age for one of the children, what could the next child's age be? It could also be 1, leaving the other child at the ripe old age of 36. Unusual, extremely unlikely – but a possibility. Continuing in this way, you will come to realise that after the first hint the insurance man knows that the correct triple of ages is one of *eight* possibilities:

Early Influences

1	1	36
1	2	18
1	3	12
1	4	9
1	6	6
2	2	9
2	3	6
3	3	4

It is now clear why he had to ask for another hint. He simply does not have enough information at this stage to choose the correct triple from this set of eight. However, we know that he was told that the sum of their ages is the number on the house next door, and we complain bitterly that *he* was able to go and look at this number but we don't get to see it. But the great thing about this puzzle is that we do – not physically, but with certainty in our minds. To find out why, let's ask what numbers he could have seen. Here they are:

$$1 + 1 + 36 = 38$$
$$1 + 2 + 18 = 21$$
$$1 + 3 + 12 = 16$$
$$1 + 4 + 9 = 14$$
$$1 + 6 + 6 = 13$$
$$2 + 2 + 9 = 13$$
$$2 + 3 + 6 = 11$$
$$3 + 3 + 4 = 10$$

Now what do you notice? If you examine the possible sums carefully, or as the textbooks often say, "the alert reader will note" that the sums are all distinct with the exception of the number 13. There are two triples whose sums are 13. Now what was the number on the house next door? It was 13! Had he seen the number 21 he would have known there and then that the ages of the children are 1, 2 and 18 and he would not have needed an extra clue. So he must have seen the number 13. Then the possibilities for the ages are $\{1, 6, 6\}$ or $\{2, 2, 9\}$. We now see the relevance of that final enough-to-put-anyone-off-clue, "The eldest plays the piano", and note that the key word is *eldest*. The family of three children whose ages are 1, 6 and 6 respectively does not have an eldest. Therefore the children are aged 2, 2 and 9. Now isn't that a nice piece of detective work?

So are you a potential cryptanalyst? The answer to the word puzzle is this:

> Not one single word in the paragraph contains the most frequently occurring letter of the English alphabet, 'e'. Furthermore, every other letter of the alphabet occurs at least once.

Try this 'cryptographic' puzzle:

The Russian Postal System Puzzle: *I heard this interesting puzzle posed by a Russian mathematician at the end of a popular talk on secrecy given one night at our local university. He told us that at one time the Russian postal system was notoriously corrupt. Any letter, package or box which was open or easily openable would be opened in the sorting office, and anything which was inside would be removed whether or not it had any value. However, since the pickings were so rich the sorters never bothered to trouble themselves with opening anything which was locked, even if they suspected it contained valuables.*

Now, Boris in Moscow had bought a beautiful gem for his girlfriend Natasha, who lived in St Petersburg, and he wanted to get it to her as quickly as possible. Neither he nor Natasha could travel to the other's city, so what was he to do? He had a strongbox with a hasp to which a number of padlocks could be attached. If he bought a padlock and key he could put the gem in the box, lock the padlock and send the box through the postal system knowing that it would not be prised open and that it would be delivered to his beloved. But what good would that do? Natasha would not have a key to open the padlock. Boris couldn't send the key separately by letter as it would be opened, and the key removed. However, Boris phoned Natasha and

Early Influences

between them they hatched a clever scheme by which they could get the precious jewel from Moscow to St Petersburg in safety despite the corrupt postal system. How did they do this?

The great thing about puzzle-solving is that it is not always the 'professional' who first finds the solution to a puzzle, or, if finding a solution, discovers the most elegant and imaginative path to its unveiling. Solving a puzzle is undertaking a journey and reaching a destination. Lacking the 'vertical' training of the academic, the amateur by necessity must be more creative and is often rewarded by finding the shortest and most beautiful route.

To illustrate this point I present two problems: one I heard in relation to the phenomenal calculating ability of the Hungarian mathematician John von Neumann; the other is mentioned in Arthur Koestler's book *The Act of Creation*. Here is the first:

The Two Trains Puzzle: *Two trains are on the same railroad track 100 km apart and heading towards each other, each at a speed of 50 km/h. A fly, initially on the front of one train, flies at 75 km/h towards the other oncoming train. On reaching it, the fly turns around (instantaneously) and flies back towards the first train. When it reaches the front of this train it turns around (again instantaneously) and flies back in the other direction. How many kilometres will it have travelled in this hectic zigzag manner before it meets its inevitable fate?*

Von Neumann is reputed to have answered "75 kilometres" immediately. When asked how he did it, he replied, "I summed the infinite series of course!" The questioner, instead of being surprised that the great man had not found the answer the 'neat way', was gobsmacked that he could actually have seen instantly that the fly travelled the ever shorter paths measuring

$$60, 12, 2\cdot4, 0\cdot48, 0\cdot096, \dots$$

and that he had summed this infinite sequence of numbers to get a total distance travelled of 75 km. What chance have the rest of us got? We may console ourselves by thinking that we would have found the smart solution: since the trains will collide in an hour, the fly travelling at 75 km/h will cover exactly 75 km. Now isn't that clever!

I'll let Arthur Koestler tell the next one in his own words.

The Buddhist Monk Puzzle: *One morning, exactly at sunrise, a Buddhist monk leaves his temple and begins to climb a tall mountain. The narrow path, no more than a foot or two wide, spiraled around the mountain to a glittering temple at the summit. The monk ascended the path at varying rates of speed, stopping many times along the way to rest and eat the dried fruit he carried with him. He reached the temple shortly before sunset. After several days of fasting he began his journey back along the same path, starting at sunrise and again walking at variable speeds with many pauses along the way, finally arriving at the lower temple just before sunset. Prove that there is a spot along the path that the monk will occupy on both trips at precisely the same time of day.*

This is a completely different puzzle to those described already. There are no numerical facts such as the monk's speed with which to begin calculating. In fact, we have no specific details of the monk's ascent or descent other than that, in both cases, he leaves at sunrise and arrives just before sunset. The time span of both journeys is the same. A trained mathematician might eventually be led to solve this problem graphically. The following solution, by a young woman with no scientific training, was described by Koestler as brilliant.

> I tried this and that, until I got fed up with the whole thing, but the image of the monk in his saffron robe walking up the hill kept persisting in my mind. Then a moment came when, superimposed on this image, I saw another, more transparent one, of the monk walking *down* the hill and I realized in a flash that the two figures *must* meet at some point some time – regardless at what speed they

walk and how often each of them stops. Then I reasoned out what I already knew: whether the monk descends two or three days later comes to the same; so I was quite justified in letting him descend on the same day, in duplicate so to speak.

Now try this one:

The Twenty People at a Party Puzzle: *Suppose there are twenty people in a room. If Alice and Bob are any two of them, and Alice knows Bob, then you may assume that Bob knows Alice. Furthermore, if Alice does not know Bob then, likewise, Bob does not know Alice. Now, any individual among these twenty may know nobody else, or some but not all of the others, or know everybody in the room. However, what might strike you as amazing on first thought is the fact that all twenty cannot each know a different number of people in the room. Put another way, there are at least two in the room who know exactly the same number of people. Can you reason out why this must be so?*

This next puzzle pits intuition against logic.

The Rope Around the Earth Puzzle: *Imagine a rope tied around the Earth's equator like a ring on a person's finger. Now imagine lifting off this very long rope (don't ask me how), cutting it somewhere so as to stitch into it exactly 1 metre of extra rope. Then imagine placing this longer rope back around the Earth at the equator. Since it is longer than the original rope by just one metre a gap between the rope and the Earth's surface will form all the way round. (Don't trouble yourself about the rope 'falling down'.) How large is the gap that is formed?*

Give an intuitive answer to this puzzle and then think carefully about it for a while. Many people find the answer so astounding that even when it is explained they are apt to say something like, "I see it but I still don't believe it."

The answer is very close to a staggering 16 cm, a little wider than this page, and obtaining it requires nothing more than knowing that the circumference of a circle of radius R is $2\pi R$. If we let R be the radius of the Earth and g be the gap size, both measured in centimetres, then (the symbol $\Rightarrow$ stands for 'implies that')

$$
\begin{aligned}
2\pi(R + g) &= 2\pi R + 100 \\
\Rightarrow 2\pi R + 2\pi g &= 2\pi R + 100 \\
\Rightarrow 2\pi g &= 100 \\
\Rightarrow g &= \frac{100}{2\pi} \approx 16
\end{aligned}
$$

Many find this answer incredible and wonder how the addition of just an extra metre can have such an effect. But as this solution reveals, the answer is independent of the length of the original rope and is one you are unlikely to forget. If instead of the Earth, a rope is tied around a football and an extra metre added as before, then the resulting gap will still be approximately 16 cm.

Magic Squares

I now present my final puzzle. This is the one from which I learned the most. Later, when asked to give talks, I found it to be the best illustrator of some of the many lessons one can learn from puzzle-solving.

Place the numbers 1 to 9 into the nine cells of a three-by-three square:

–	–	–
–	–	–
–	–	–

so that the sum of the entries along
  - *each of the three rows*
  - *each of the three columns*
  - *each of the two diagonals*
is 15.

   "Can it be done?" I hear you ask.
   "Amazingly, yes."

A square in which each of the eight possible sums is 15 is known as a three-by-three *Magic Square,* and the sum 15 is said to be the *magic sum*. I'll tell you later how to figure out why this magic sum is 15 and not some other number.
   The square

5	6	4
9	7	8
1	2	3

is not a magic square because it does not meet all eight 'magic conditions'. Although its three columns sum to 15, one row sums to 15 and one diagonal sums to 15, there are two rows and one diagonal whose sums are not 15.
   As a start to solving this problem, simply use trial and error. Do not give up if you do not find a solution quickly, but keep trying – remember, it can be done.
   After many attempts to place the nine numbers in the square you might begin to realise that the central cell holds the key to solving this puzzle. This cell is *unique* in that it is the only cell that touches all the other cells:

In Code

Consequently, whatever number is placed in this cell gets added to each of the remaining numbers along some row, column or diagonal. This is an important observation. Let us see which numbers can be placed in this cell. Can the number 6 be placed in the central cell, as shown?

–	–	–
–	6	–
–	–	–

No! Why not? Think carefully before reading any further.

If you are still at a loss, look at the diagram and ask yourself, "If 6 is in the central cell, where can I place the number 9?"

Nowhere! The number 9 must be placed in one of the surrounding cells but when added to the 6 in the centre, a sum of 15 is obtained with just *two* numbers. This observation is a big breakthrough because for the very same reason the central cell cannot contain the number 7, 8 or 9 as two numbers alone would then sum to 15 or more, along one of the rows, columns or diagonals. The trouble is simply that each of the numbers 6, 7, 8 and 9 is too big to go in the centre. Now isn't that a nice piece of reasoning, blending simple arithmetic with the geometry of the cells?

Can any of the numbers 1, 2, 3 and 4 be placed in the central cell? Maybe these numbers are too small.

Let us be specific. Can we place 4 in the central cell? No, for then where can the 1 go? Nowhere, because $1 + 4 = 5$ leaves us looking for a 10 to make a sum of 15, and 'there ain't no 10'. This is great. Better still, the situation is the same with 3, 2 or 1 in the centre. Thus we have discovered that neither 6, 7, 8, 9 nor 4, 3, 2, 1 can go in the central cell.

Using a little logic, we now know that our only chance of success is to place the middle number 5 in the central cell:

Doing this does not guarantee success but it is necessary. It remains to be seen if it will be sufficient. Even at this stage we have learned a valuable lesson: "A little thinking can save a lot of computing."

Knowing that the number 5 must go in the central cell is a huge step forward. Rather than resume the trial-and-error approach, try to make further progress by doing some more thinking. Think of it as smart detective work.

Maybe there are restrictions on where some of the other numbers may be placed. The number 9, being the biggest, might be worth further investigation. Where can the number 9 be placed? In a corner cell?

Let us see if we can place the number 9 in a corner cell:

9	–	–
–	5	–
–	–	*

If so, the cell marked with a * must contain the number 1 (why?). Thus we have the following diagram:

In Code

9	–	–
–	5	x
–	x	1

Now here comes a killer observation: the numbers 6, 7 and 8 are too big to share a row or column with 9 so they must occupy the two cells marked with x. But 'three into two won't go': we cannot place three numbers in two cells. We have made another major step forward. The number 9 cannot be placed in a corner cell.

So, using simple reasoning and the minimum of computation, we now know that the number

- 5 must go into the central cell
- 9 must go into one of the central side cells

Try

A	–	–
9	5	1
B	–	–

where, in the first column, we have labelled the companion entries to 9 as A and B for further scrutiny. Resist the temptation to stop reasoning and don't simply finish the puzzle off by testing a few numbers. Do a little more detective work because it is proving very worthwhile.

The numbers A and B in the first column cannot be any of 6, 7 or 8 (why?). Hence they must be 2, 3 or 4. But A cannot be 3 because then B would have to be 3 also, which is impossible since 3 can be used only once. Thus A *must* be 4 or 2 (in which case B is either 2 or 4, respectively).

Victory is in sight. Let's choose A to be 4. We are now at this stage:

4	–	–
9	5	1
2	–	–

Now, where all the remaining numbers go is forced, so we may say that the square 'completes itself':

4	3	8
9	5	1
2	7	6

Pure Magic!

After I first solved this problem by the trial-and-error method, Dad took me through the puzzle slowly just as I have done above. He wanted to show me how sometimes 'things can be reasoned out'. It was a wonderful lesson and convinced me of the importance of standing back from a problem to think about it rather than rushing at it. Sometimes I still like to just dive in because it's great fun fiddling around with numbers, but if you really want to make inroads on a particular problem it is better to stop and reflect. It was fantastic to see what pure thought alone could achieve. I immediately wanted more problems of this type, but Dad said that there was still more to be had from this magic square puzzle. In fact the best was yet to come: with a little more thinking we could say exactly how many three-by-three magic squares there are in all. This unexpected bonus would come as a result of having thought the problem through from beginning to end, without having run off at some stage to finish it by plugging in numbers until a combination which works was found. Had we done this we'd have missed out on seeing deeper into the problem and proving, almost without realising it, the 'little theorem' which says that there are exactly eight three-by-three magic squares.

In Code

"Why eight?" I asked myself. Well, let's see. For starters, there is no choice in where the 5 must go: it must always be placed in the central cell. However, there are exactly four choices of cell for the number 9. When this is chosen the position of the number 1 is automatically determined, as are the two possible cell choices for the number 4. When a cell is chosen for the number 4 there are no further cell choices for the remaining numbers. Since any of the first four choices for the 9 can be combined with any of the two choices for the 4, there are in all 4 × 2 = 8 possible three-by-three magic squares. That is all there is to it, but what a thrill to know why!

Here are the eight solutions:

8	1	6
3	5	7
4	9	2

6	7	2
1	5	9
8	3	4

2	9	4
7	5	3
6	1	8

4	3	8
9	5	1
2	7	6

4	9	2
3	5	7
8	1	6

6	1	8
7	5	3
2	9	4

2	7	6
9	5	1
4	3	8

8	3	4
1	5	9
6	7	2

These eight solutions are related to one another. Suppose the original solution we found was:

8	1	6
3	5	7
4	9	2

Then the first four solutions listed are obtained from this solution by leaving it alone or rotating the square anticlockwise through 90°, 180° and 270°, respectively. (Of course when you do this you have to 'stand the numbers up properly' again.)

Thus

8	1	6
3	5	7
4	9	2

6	7	2
1	5	9
8	3	4

2	9	4
7	5	3
6	1	8

4	3	8
9	5	1
2	7	6

are the solutions obtained by rotating the original solution. The second set of four solutions,

4	9	2
3	5	7
8	1	6

6	1	8
7	5	3
2	9	4

2	7	6
9	5	1
4	3	8

8	3	4
1	5	9
6	7	2

is obtained from the original solution by reflections in the middle row, middle column and in the two diagonals. In the first of these squares the middle row is the same as the middle row of the original square, while in the second the middle column is the same as the middle column of the original square. In the third the diagonal running from SW to NE is the same as the corresponding diagonal in the original square, while in the fourth the diagonal running from NW to SE is the same as that in the original square.

If you know from geometry that a square has eight symmetries (I won't go into why) then you will realise that the eight solutions given above really amount to only *one*. Once you find one solution, as we have done, then you get the other seven for free simply by exploiting the symmetries of a square. We have already explained how this is done when we discussed rotations and reflections. This is why mathematicians say that there is only one solution 'up to symmetry'. Note that the number 5 never leaves the central square under any of the transformations. Thus we could say that there is really only *one* magic square.

In Code

To finish off, let us answer the question,

Why is 15 the magic sum for a three-by-three magic square?

Suppose the magic sum is M. Then the entries across the top row sum to M, as do the entries across the middle row and the bottom row. When you total the sums for the three rows you get $3M$. However, when you total the three rows together, you are also summing the first nine natural numbers in some order:

$$3M = 1 + 2 + 3 + 4 + 5 + 6 + 7 + 8 + 9$$
$$\Rightarrow 3M = 45$$
$$\Rightarrow M = 15$$

Voilà!

You can appreciate fully what has been accomplished when I tell you that there are

$$9 \times 8 \times 7 \times 6 \times 5 \times 4 \times 3 \times 2 \times 1 = 362880$$

different ways to place the numbers 1 to 9 into the nine cells of a three-by-three square. Because each square gives rise to eight configurations, one-eighth of this number, 45360, is the number of genuinely different squares. Only one of these is a magic square. It is intriguing that there is one and only one magic square. After all, there was no reason at the outset to believe that there had to be even one. Or was there?

This problem is a fine example of how, with reasoning, a multitude of possibilities can be narrowed down to just a few candidates. You could solve this problem by programming a computer to generate all 362880 possible squares, test the eight row, column and diagonal sums of each square and select only those for which all eight sums are 15. Although the enormous computer calculation will give the eight solutions, it can never explain why only eight are found. To answer this, you, the human being, have to think about the problem.

Early Influences

Puzzles, like humour, have a universal appeal and know of no boundaries – cultural, educational or otherwise. People of all ages and levels of education are attracted to the puzzle as they are to the joke. In a sense, there is an affinity between the two in that a vital ingredient of both is the element of surprise. No problem is worthy of the name 'puzzle' if its solution is obvious, just as the joke whose punchline is easily anticipated is soon forgotten. The true puzzle should be accessible to all; its solution should require no specialist knowledge other than, at times, the rudiments of arithmetic and algebra. It is perhaps the unconscious feeling that we all start out equal that gives puzzles their charm.

2. Mathematical Excursions

God made the natural numbers, all the rest is the work of Man.

LEOPOLD KRONECKER

*T*hese were the first words – a bit alarmingly, in German – that my father wrote on the board on the evening of my first class at the Cork Institute of Technology, where he lectures in mathematics. He explained that Kronecker was a German mathematician who lived in the nineteenth century. Little did I know the role the natural numbers,

$$1, 2, 3, \ldots$$

were to play in my life over the next two years.

Although, as I have already said, I had often been taught or helped with my school mathematics by my father at home, this was the first time I had ever attended a formal lecture of his and seen him present work in an organised way in front of a group of people. This unusual evening class had come about as a result of a conversation he and I had during the previous summer which went something like, "Now that you have decided to do Transition year, I must do some maths with you." In the Irish school system there is an optional year, called Transition year, which comes at the end of the Junior cycle (the first three years) and before the Senior cycle (the last two years). He continued, " I'd like to show you how some beautiful but reasonably elementary mathematics is applied, stuff that you wouldn't ordinarily come across in school."

Not knowing exactly what he had in mind, but not wishing to be collared and brought to the blackboard in the kitchen at random times, I replied, "Dad, whatever you do, do something structured!"

He promised to think carefully about how best to approach, in a gentle way, giving me a realistic glimpse into the mathematical world. Conscious of how much he would have appreciated it had someone done this for him thirty years ago, he felt obliged now to offer me the benefit of his mathematical knowledge. "Of course, only if you are genuinely interested, I wouldn't force it on you."

Of course not! But I was interested. So this is how the evening class was conceived, and this is how I was to be introduced to many wonderful mathematical ideas – ideas which were accessible and which I might never otherwise have encountered unless I chose to pursue mathematics as a career.

The title for the intended series of lectures, 'Mathematical Excursions', was suggested by a book by Robert M. Young called *Excursions in Calculus* which is a favourite of Dad's. It was not the intention to present mathematics in a very rigorous fashion, but rather to explore 'elementary' aspects of 'higher' mathematics and learn how these ideas find applications in different fields of study outside mathematics. Beyond a thorough grounding in the skills of ordinary arithmetic and basic algebra, the only other essential prerequisite for undertaking these excursions was interest. The primary aim of the course was that everybody take pleasure in sharing in the spirit of discovery.

The class consisted of about eight people of whom I, at fifteen and a half, was the youngest, though there were one or two others nearly as young. The rest were adults of various backgrounds: one was a secondary school mathematics teacher, one a chemistry graduate working in a medical laboratory, others were computer scientists. All were there either because they had loved maths at school but hadn't continued with it or because they felt they hadn't properly appreciated the subject the first time round. This class, which was not part of any course, led to no award or certification at its completion and made no demands whatsoever by way of homework or study, may have seemed an ideal way of 'getting back into maths' in an easy going, informal manner. We were told at the outset that there would be no pressure to perform, and that we need not fear being asked questions but we could ask them at any time. We were to feel free to say 'any crazy thing we liked' and we were not to be in the least afraid of appearing to make fools of ourselves. In fact, the more you are prepared to make a fool of yourself the more you'll learn. These reassuring statements made me quite sure that I was going to enjoy my next few Tuesday nights, even if I was not completely comfortable with the fact that my father was the lecturer. In school, students always pity those who have to endure classes given by their parents, though I'm sure such a situation is worse for the parent who is the teacher.

The first excursions were to be in elementary number theory, with some aspects of cryptography as their final destination. Along the way we would see interesting sights, rich in their own right regardless of whether or not they had immediate application. Dad told us that when he was a student, number theory was regarded as the sole province of mathematicians, and those who devoted their lives to its study were considered the purest of the pure, so few were its perceived applications. He said that in the 1960s engineers and scientists had begun to find applications of number theory, and that at the end of the 1970s the discipline came of age, in the applied sense, with the advent of public key cryptography. Now millions of dollars were being set aside by the U.S. Government for the study of cryptography, a subject which is full of wonderful ideas and about which, he said, he could hardly wait to tell us. Whereas in the past many great number theorists had barely made a living, their modern counterparts were now being actively sought out, so great was the demand for expertise in this emerging science of secrecy which relied so fundamentally on the branch of mathematics that the great universal mathematician Gauss (of whom more later) revered above all else. It was he who said that

Mathematical Excursions

Mathematics is the queen of the sciences and number theory is the queen of mathematics.

As you might imagine, hearing all this filled me with curiosity and interest. Mom said it was like the Sleeping Beauty fairy tale, and she was prompted to write:

> A princess was the Theory of Number,
>   whom no practical use did encumber,
> 'til Cryptography the prince
>   ('tis all secrecy since),
> did kiss her awake from her slumber.

I thought about those who had toiled away through the centuries at unravelling the mysteries of this subject, motivated by nothing more than a passionate desire to know. They could have hardly dreamt of the applications that some of their results would one day find. I wondered what it was they had discovered, and what they would think if they could see how some of these discoveries are now being used. I was eager to learn the subject and surmise for myself whether they would be surprised or not.

We were at once tantalised and put on our guard by the warning that number theory is notoriously deceptive. We were told that very soon we'd find ourselves asking *simple* questions, many of which others would have asked before us over the ages, and some of which to this day have still not been answered.

Of Prime Importance

Our mathematical excursion begins with the natural numbers.

A natural number is *divisible* by another natural number if and only if the first number is a 'natural' multiple of the second one. Thus 98 is divisible by 7 because when 7 is multiplied by 14 the result is 98. In this case the number 7 is said to be a *factor* or a *divisor* of 98. By the same token, 14 is also a factor or divisor of 98. Because 98 = 98 × 1 the numbers 1 and 98 are also factors of 98. They are termed the trivial or improper factors of 98 because of their obviousness and the fact that there is no labour required to find them. On the other hand the factors 7 and 14 are termed non-trivial or proper factors of 98.

We often say that 98 is the *product* of its factors 7 and 14, while we refer to 7 × 14 as a *proper* factorisation of 98. An improper or trivial factorisation is 1 × 98 (which is the same as 98 × 1). Two other proper factors of 98 are 2 and 49, with 2 being the smallest non-trivial factor of 98, and 49 the largest. Thus 2 × 49 is another proper factorisation of 98.

The natural number 99 is not divisible by 7 because there is no natural number which when multiplied by 7 gives 99. Thus 7 is not a factor or divisor of 99. However, 3 is a factor of 99, as is 11, but whereas 11 is termed a *single* factor of 99, the factor 3 is a *repeated* factor because 3 × 3 = 9 is also a factor of 99.

Every natural number greater than 1 is always divisible by itself and 1, and so always has at least two factors and a trivial factorisation. However, among the natural numbers there are many which have more than just the two trivial factors. As we have just seen, 98 is one such number. Another example is the number 12, which has exactly six factors. They are 1, 2, 3, 4, 6 and 12; the four factors 2, 3, 4 and 6 are the proper factors of 12, while 1 and 12 are its improper or trivial factors. The fact that so many lesser numbers divide 'evenly' into 12 was one reason why the old English shilling was equal to 12 pennies.

Can you find the number less than 1000 which has the most factors? I won't tell you the answer, but I will tell you that it has 32 factors. If this strikes you as a little too much like work, or not particularly interesting, don't worry – just read on. (If you'd like to know more, see Appendix B.)

There are also natural numbers which have *no more* than the two trivial factors. Of the first thirty-eight natural numbers,

Mathematical Excursions

1, **2**, **3**, 4, **5**, 6, **7**, 8, 9, 10, **11**, 12, **13**, 14, 15, 16, **17**, 18, **19**, 20, 21, 22, **23**, 24, 25, 26, 27, 28, **29**, 30, **31**, 32, 33, 34, 35, 36, **37**, 38

those printed in bold, namely

2, 3, 5, 7, 11, 13, 17, 19, 23, 29, 31, 37

have exactly two factors. These numbers are the first dozen of what are known as the *prime numbers*. We emphasise that a prime number, or *prime* for short, is a natural number which has only two factors, itself and 1. Thus a prime cannot be written as the product of numbers smaller than itself. As we shall see, the primes are the elite of the natural numbers.

Those numbers which have more than two factors are known as *composite numbers*. Thus 12 and 98 are composite numbers. We can make a geometric distinction between prime numbers and composite numbers. A row of 12 coins

can be arranged into a rectangular array consisting of three rows each with exactly four coins:

This is possible because 12 is *composite* (short for composite number) and so has a non-trivial factorisation given by $12 = 4 \times 3$.

This row of 12 coins can also be arranged as

which consists of three rows of four, and reflects the fact that $12 = 3 \times 4$. Note that this arrangement is the previous one rotated through 90° so that the rows become columns and vice versa.

Another arrangement is

which may be thought of as two rows with 6 coins each or six columns with 2 coins each. The rectangle is a geometric illustration of the fact that $12 = 2 \times 6 = 6 \times 2$.

On the other hand, a row consisting of a prime number of coins can never be rearranged into a rectangular array with more than one row where each row has the same number of coins. Add just one more coin to the row of 12 coins above to get a row of 13 coins

● ● ● ● ● ● ● ● ● ● ● ● ●

and, try as you will, you will never succeed in rearranging this single row into a rectangular array of more than one row with each row having the same number of coins.

You might think that because a number is 'big' it is bound to have lots of factors, but surprisingly this is not always true. The number 889363, which is not far off a million, has only its two trivial factors. It has no proper factors. A single row of 889363 soldiers could never be rearranged into ranks and files so that each file contains the same number of soldiers. Thus 889363 is another example of a prime. If you add one more soldier, then you can form a rectangle consisting of 644 rows each with 1381 soldiers, or a rectangle with 161 rows each with 5524 soldiers. Are there other rectangular arrangements?

The natural number 2 is the only *even* prime number and so is considered the *oddest* prime of all. Pairs, such as $\{3, 5\}, \{5, 7\}$ and $\{11, 13\}$, in which the larger prime of the pair is greater than the smaller one by exactly 2 are termed *twin primes*.

Now that we know the difference between a prime number and

a composite number we can ask all sorts of questions, two of which might be:

- How do you factorise a number?
- How many prime numbers are there?

You might think that to answer the first question is easy, but it is in fact one of the most difficult and important problems in number theory. The second, which may strike you as harder, was answered over two thousand years ago.

So you see that although we have barely begun to talk about numbers, we are already posing questions which appear simple but whose answers are far from immediate, and may even elude us. As the mathematician Paul Erdös, known as the Magician from Budapest, remarked "Babies can ask questions about primes which grown men cannot answer."

Some other questions are:

- How do you decide whether or not a number is prime?
- How many prime numbers are there less than a given number?
- Is there a formula for generating prime numbers?
- Is there an infinite number of twin primes?

The assertion that the answer to the last question is 'yes' is known as the twin prime conjecture because nobody has been able to pronounce on it yet one way or the other. As Peter Rosenthal wrote,

> The infinitude of the primes
> Is the subject of plenty of rhymes,
>   But we can't begin
>   To prove there's a twin
> An infinite number of times.

The number 420 is composite because it can be written as 10×42. Another non-trivial factorisation which also reveals 420 to be composite is 14×30. This factorisation looks as if it has nothing in common with the previous one and so might lead one to believe that 420 can be constructed in different ways. However, neither of these apparently different factorisations is *complete* because, in each case, the factors in the products can themselves be 'broken down' or decomposed by further factorisation. A factorisation is complete only when all the factors appearing in the final product are primes. This is because primes cannot be factored non-trivially. Primes are to atoms what composites are to molecules. Doing this for the number 420, starting with each of the incomplete factorisations given above, we get

$$420 = 10 \times 42$$
$$= (2 \times 5) \times (3 \times 14)$$
$$= 2 \times 5 \times 3 \times (2 \times 7)$$

and

$$420 = 14 \times 30$$
$$= (2 \times 7) \times (5 \times 6)$$
$$= 2 \times 7 \times 5 \times (2 \times 3)$$

Both these combinations of primes, when arranged in order of increasing magnitude, give

$$420 = 2 \times 2 \times 3 \times 5 \times 7$$

Here 420 is represented in a unique way as a product of primes. Had we begun with $420 = 15 \times 28$, we would still have arrived at this same *prime decomposition* of 420.

Every natural number has a unique prime decomposition, which is something that may seem self-evident but is in fact far from obvious. The uniqueness of the complete factorisation of an integer is something very fundamental which had to be proved. It is known as the *fundamental theorem of arithmetic* or the *unique factorisation theorem*.

So every natural number is made from a unique combination of prime numbers, and we may think of the primes as the building blocks for all the numbers. I must admit that I wondered how things could be otherwise. But who can say without proof that the number

$$654298765432987654321111398503400542111$$

can be decomposed in one way only? Isn't it conceivable that two or more different combinations of primes might, when multiplied out, give this answer? The fact that this *cannot* happen is very important when it comes to cracking cryptographic codes.

To help you appreciate fully this unique factorisation property of the natural numbers, let me tell you about the *Hilbert numbers*, the first few of which are

$$1, 5, 9, 13, 17, 21, 25, 29, 33, 37, 41, 45, 49, 53, 57, \ldots$$

Apart from 1, each of these numbers is 4 times a natural number plus 1, e.g. $45 = 4 \times 11 + 1$. If you multiply any two of these numbers you always get another one of the same type. (This is not hard to show using a little basic algebra.) Focusing solely on these numbers – and imagining that no other numbers such as 3 and 7 exist – we can, as with the natural numbers, talk about *Hilbert primes* such as 5, 9, 13 and 17 (no one of these is divisible by a smaller Hilbert number other than 1) and *Hilbert composites* such as 45 (which is the product of the two Hilbert primes, 5 and 9). Now comes a surprise. The calculation

$$1617 = 21 \times 77 = 33 \times 49$$

shows that the Hilbert number 1617 can be completely factorised as a product of Hilbert primes in *two different ways*. The numbers 21, 33, 49 and 77 are all Hilbert primes (though none of them is a natural prime).

Because of this lack of unique factorisation, arithmetic with Hilbert numbers might prove a tad more complicated, if not more interesting. Maybe we should use this arithmetic to confuse our enemies. "Which two Hilbert primes did I multiply to get 1617?"

Whichever way they answer we can say, "Sorry, wrong" and give the other combination.

How Do You Decide Whether or Not a Number is Prime?

"Simple. Step I: check whether it is divisible by 2. If it is, it is composite (unless of course it's 2 but, come on, let's be serious). If it is not, proceed to Step II: check whether it is divisible by 3. If it is, it is composite. If not, proceed to Step III: check whether it is divisible by 5."

"Hold on a second! You've just skipped 4. What about checking whether it is divisible by 4?"

"There's no need. If it's not divisible by 2, then it certainly is not divisible by 4. If it's divisible by 5, then it's composite; otherwise proceed …"

"Don't tell me. Step IV: check whether it's divisible by 7, the next prime after 5."

"Yes."

"But this checking to see whether the number is divisible by primes could go on for a long time if the number is large. And wouldn't I need to know a lot of primes?"

"You do need to have a store of primes for the purposes of this *trial division* procedure. But leaving that problem aside for the moment, how many tests would you have to carry out to determine whether or not 149 is prime?"

"You might have to divide 149 by all the primes up to 149."

"That would certainly tell you whether 149 is prime, but the good news is that there is no need to do this much work. Ask yourself, 'Could 23 be the first prime factor of 149?'"

"Why not?"

"Well, if 23 were the first factor then the other factor would have to be at least 23. But $23 \times 23 = 529$, which is much bigger than 149."

"Oh! I see. So how far up do you have to test?"

"If 149 has factors, then not all of them can be greater than its square root."

"So, up as far as the square root of the number."

"Yes. Now, $\sqrt{149} = 12 \cdot 2 \dots$, so if 149 is composite it must have a prime factor less than 13. So I need only test to see whether it's divisible by the primes 2, 3, 5, 7 and 11. I need do at most five trial divisions to decide whether or not 149 is prime."

"And since it's not divisible by any of these five primes, the number 149 must also be a prime. You can add this to your collection of prime numbers and use it as a trial divisor in other calculations testing numbers which are larger than $149^2 = 22{,}201$."

"So this procedure will either find a prime factor of the number being tested or establish that the number itself is a prime."

"Yes. This procedure is called the trial division algorithm. An algorithm is just a fancy word for a step-by-step procedure."

"That's great. With super-fast computers you should be able to test any number fairly quickly."

"Unfortunately, it is practical to use this algorithm only on reasonably small numbers. This is the bad news about this wonderfully simple procedure. Even if you avoid storing huge amounts of primes in the computer's memory by getting the computer to divide the number being tested by *every* number up to its square root, it can take a very long time for numbers with as few as 40 digits. Let me quote the number-theorist Carl Pomerance:

> The main drawback of the trial division algorithm is that it takes too long if a number has *no small prime factors*. For example, say we use the trial division algorithm on a computer that can do one million trial divisions per second to determine if a given number is prime or composite. If the number is a prime near 10^{40} (a number with approximately 40 digits), the running time will be about one million years while if it's a prime near 10^{50} (a number with approximately 50 digits), the age of the universe would not suffice.

That's pretty bleak. Although in theory it is simple to decide whether or not a natural number is prime, this method is not practical.

In Code

The Sieve of Eratosthenes

Around 250 BC, the Greek mathematician Eratosthenes used a spectacularly simple method to find primes which has become known as the *sieve of Eratosthenes*. Here is how it finds all the prime numbers among the first 120 numbers, which are listed, with the exception of the number 1, in the following array:

–	**2**	3	4	5	6	7	8	9	10
11	12	13	14	15	16	17	18	19	20
21	22	23	24	25	26	27	28	29	30
31	32	33	34	35	36	37	38	39	40
41	42	43	44	45	46	47	48	49	50
51	52	53	54	55	56	57	58	59	60
61	62	63	64	65	66	67	68	69	70
71	72	73	74	75	76	77	78	79	80
81	82	83	84	85	86	87	88	89	90
91	92	93	94	95	96	97	98	99	100
101	102	103	104	105	106	107	108	109	110
111	112	113	114	115	116	117	118	119	120

The even numbers 4, 6, 8, 10, … are all composite since their respective factoristaions are 2×2, 2×3, 2×4, 2×5, and so on. The first sieving, 'based on the prime' **2**, proceeds as follows: Beginning with the number 4, 'sieve' or delete every *second* number by leaving the corresponding cell blank. This operation of skipping over numbers or cells to reach other ones involves nothing more than counting. When this is done the original array becomes

-	2	3		5		7		9	
11		13		15		17		19	
21		23		25		27		29	
31		33		35		37		39	
41		43		45		47		49	
51		53		55		57		59	
61		63		65		67		69	
71		73		75		77		79	
81		83		85		87		89	
91		93		95		97		99	
101		103		105		107		109	
111		113		115		117		119	

Since the number **3** has not been sieved, it is the next prime and is used for the second sieving. Now empty every *third* cell after 3: one, two, delete, one, two, delete, and so on. It doesn't matter if a cell, such as that corresponding to 6, is already blank. The reason blank cells (corresponding to numbers which have already been sieved out) are never removed is to ensure that the skipping proceeds correctly at all stages. The blank cells are a vital record of where numbers were. After this second sieving, the array becomes

-	2	3		5		7			
11		13				17		19	
		23		25				29	
31				35		37			
41		43				47		49	
		53		55				59	
61				65		67			
71		73				77		79	
		83		85				89	
91				95		97			
101		103				107		109	
		113		115				119	

It is worth noting that the first number to be sieved by this second sieving based on 3 is its square, $9 = 3^2 = 3 \times 3$.

Since the number **5** has not been sieved by either of the two previous sievings, it must be the third prime and the basis for the next sieving. Leaving every *fifth* cell after 5 blank, the following array emerges:

–	**2**	**3**		**5**		7			
11		13				17		19	
		23						29	
31						37			
41		43				47		49	
		53						59	
61						67			
71		73				77		79	
		83						89	
91						97			
101		103				107		109	
		113						119	

This time the first number to bite the dust, having survived the previous two sievings, is $25 = 5^2 = 5 \times 5$. Now **7** is the first number appearing after 2, 3 and 5 in this latest array. Since it has survived all three previous sievings, it must be the next prime. Leaving every *seventh* cell after 7 blank gives the following array:

–	2	3		5		7			
11		13				17		19	
		23						29	
31						37			
41		43				47			
		53						59	
61						67			
71		73						79	
		83						89	
						97			
101		103				107		109	
		113							

Again note that the first new number deleted when skipping in sevens is 7^2 or 49. Now stop. Why? Because the next sieving, based on the prime 11, crosses out every eleventh number after 11. The first multiple of 11 which isn't already sieved is the eleventh; the lower multiples of 11 have already been deleted by those sievings based on one or other of the primes 2, 3, 5 and 7. Hence 121 (11^2) is the next natural number for the chop, so those thirty numbers less than 121 clearly visible in the last array are in no further danger. These survivors are the thirty primes less than 120. It took just four sievings to reveal them. (Do you now see why the first 120 numbers were chosen to demonstrate this remarkably simple algorithm?)

Although the sieve of Eratosthenes may look a very laborious method, it is in fact a very fast procedure since, by contrast with the method of trial division, it does not make use of time-consuming divisions. It is a very nice programming exercise to get this working and fine-tuned. When you do get it going, it works a treat and lists all the primes up to a given number in no time. It will fill the screen with the 1229 primes less than 10,000 before you have time to catch your breath. The fact that its output can be huge is something of a disadvantage, but I'm told that this simple principle is the basis of a very powerful modern method used in the constant quest for larger and larger primes.

I was to learn a lot about the difference between theory and practice during my first project in cryptography. I would come to appreciate that it wasn't good enough to know any old way of doing something – you have to find methods or techniques that implement the theory in highly efficient ways. This 'real-life' aspect caught my interest. Great theory, but is it implementable? It's no use receiving a secret message scrambled in a highly secure way which says, "Evacuate immediately!" if it is going to take a day to work out what it is saying.

But there is some good news. The amazing thing is that there are other ways of figuring out whether or not a number is prime which work quite speedily on large numbers. But this is a story for later.

Is There an Infinite Number of Prime Numbers?

Although the ancients were able to find many primes with the sieve method, and today we actually know millions upon millions of primes, might it not be the case that they run out? This would mean that there is a highest prime number, after which all the remaining numbers stretching to infinity are composite. So is there only a finite number of primes, or is there an infinite number of them? I remember thinking how you would go about answering questions such as these. Do they necessarily have answers? I know that logically you can say that there is either an infinite number of primes or there isn't; it must be one or the other, but maybe it is not within our power to say which is the case. Subconsciously I wondered how people long since dead could have found answers to such questions.

Over two thousand years ago the Greek mathematician Euclid, who lived in Alexandria in Egypt, published in the sixth volume of his famous book on geometry a wonderfully simple proof that there is an infinite number of primes. You can find this proof in text books on number theory, but you can also find an excellent explanation of this beautiful result in Simon Singh's book *Fermat's Last Theorem*. (If you don't have a copy, you should get one because it's a great book.) Euclid's proof is an example of a 'proof by contradiction'. He begins by assuming that there is only a finite number of primes and then, by a simple but clever argument, shows that this assumption leads to a contradiction. Consequently there must be an infinite number of primes. It is a wonderful non-constructive proof: it does not construct or exhibit an infinite set of primes explicitly, it just convinces you that there has to be an infinite number of them. It is an example of an 'existence proof'. It is similar to proving that there are at least two people in Dublin with the same number of hairs on their heads, without actually producing two such people. You may know with certainty that they are out there somewhere but please don't ask me to find them!

Is There a Formula for Generating Prime Numbers?

Knowing that there is an infinite number of primes is a different thing to knowing how to find any of them. Some gallant attempts have been made to find formulae which generate prime numbers only. Pierre Fermat (1601–1665), the great French mathematician renowned for his famous Last Theorem, mistakenly believed that each time a natural number n is substituted in the formula

$$F(n) = 2^{2^n} + 1$$

a prime is generated. Here $F(n)$ does not mean F multiplied by n, which would be written $F \times n$ or Fn. Read $F(n)$ as 'the nth Fermat number'. Then $F(1)$ is the first Fermat number, $F(2)$ is the second Fermat number, and so on. Fermat wasn't asserting that this formula would supply *all* the prime numbers, only that it would always produce a prime number each time a different natural number n is substituted into the formula. Of course, if he could have proved his assertion he would have had a proof different from Euclid's that there is an infinite number of primes.

Substituting 1 for n in the above formula gives

In Code

$$F(1) = 2^{2^1} + 1 = 2^2 + 1 = 4 + 1 = 5$$

So the first Fermat number, $F(1)$, is 5, which is a prime. The Fermat numbers obtained when 1, 2, 3 and 4 are substituted for n in turn in the above formula (note that 2^{2^3} means $2^{(2^3)}$ and not $(2^2)^3$) are

$$F(1) = 2^{2^1} + 1 = 2^2 + 1 = 4 + 1 = 5$$
$$F(2) = 2^{2^2} + 1 = 2^4 + 1 = 16 + 1 = 17$$
$$F(3) = 2^{2^3} + 1 = 2^8 + 1 = 256 + 1 = 257$$
$$F(4) = 2^{2^4} + 1 = 2^{16} + 1 = 65536 + 1 = 65537$$

These Fermat numbers are all prime. Now, $n = 5$ and $n = 6$ generate

$$F(5) = 2^{2^5} + 1 = 2^{32} + 1 = 4294967297$$
$$F(6) = 2^{2^6} + 1 = 2^{64} + 1 = 18446744073709551617$$

the first of which is a ten-digit number which Fermat believed to be prime, and the second is a twenty-digit number which was well beyond the ability of anybody to factorise in the 1640s, or in fact at any time before the advent of computers in the twentieth century. However, it is surprising that he did not discover that 641 is a factor of $F(5) = 4294967297$ because when challenged by his compatriot Father Mersenne (1588–1648) to factorise the larger twelve-digit number 100895598169, he gave the factorisation 112303 × 898423. The smaller factor 112303 of the twelve-digit number is much larger than 641. (The number 112303 is the 10650th prime, while 641 is only the 116th prime.) Perhaps Fermat didn't try very hard. If he mistakenly bypassed 641 when testing $F(5) = 4294967297$ to see whether it is a prime, then it is understandable why he would have pronounced $F(5)$ to be prime. Its one remaining factor is the seven-digit prime 6700417 (the 457523rd prime).

It was the Swiss mathematician Leonhard Euler (1707–1783) who, almost a century later in 1732, found the prime factors 641 and 6700417 of $F(5)$. The fact that it was nearly a hundred years before someone found how to factorise $F(5)$ is an indication that factorising may not in general be an easy task. (Of course, you might say that nobody could be bothered to try.)

What about the number $F(6)=18446744073709551617$, or 'Fermat-six' as it is now known? It is not a prime. Its factorisation was found by the eighty-two-year-old F. Landry in the nineteenth century. So that you can appreciate what an impressive feat this was, I am going to ask you to imagine that you are thrown into prison and are told that you'll get out when you find the factorisation. How long a sentence do you think you'd serve? Initially you'd be very despondent, believing that your sentence amounted to life imprisonment. In time, you might grow hopeful of an early release, particularly if you know that an eighty-two-year-old was able to factorise this number before the era of calculators and computers. If he was able to factorise the number then you should also be able to do so. But maybe he knew more maths than you do. Quite possibly. Basic arithmetic – along with an unknown amount of mental labour – is all that is needed to gain freedom. You'd certainly get to know a few things about numbers, and you might discover that you had hidden talents.

My father often used this 'prison question' during his lectures when he wanted to emphasise that something which was now known to us was at one time far from obvious, and that its attainment is still worthy of great admiration. By the way, here is the result of Landry's labours:

$$18446744073709551617 = 274177 \times 67280421310721$$

In the past, the intractability of factorising a number would have been viewed as somewhat disappointing because the prevailing spirit was one of complete optimism that all problems, no matter how hard they appeared to be, would eventually yield to analysis and ingenuity. But now, rather than being downcast, we turn the tables around and exploit the very difficulty of factorising. This is what three students at the Massachusetts Institute of Technology (MIT), Ronald Rivest, Adi Shamir and Leonard Adelman, did in 1977 when they invented a famous cryptosystem based on the tremendous difficulty of factorising large numbers. In August 1977, in a *Scientific American* article, Martin Gardner described this wonderful system and published a 129-digit number which came to be known as RSA129 (after the initials of the inventors' surnames and the length of the number). The reader was told that this number is the product of two primes. If one could factorise the number one could decode a certain secret message and claim a $100 prize. (I thought this rather a paltry reward, but I could hear my father saying, "The real reward is the joy of solving the problem.") To quote Barry Cipra, writing in 1997,

> That $100 looked safe, at least for the next 20,000 years or so ... Not so. The RSA challenge yielded a mere 17 years later to a calculation that took less than a year from start to finish. A loosely organized group of factoring afficionados, numbering over 600 individuals in more than two dozen countries, nailed the 64- and 65-digit prime factors of RSA129 in an eight month effort, ending in April, 1994.

Although the twenty-thousand-year time estimate proved way off the mark, this quote underlines the great difficulty of factorising numbers in excess of 100 digits. Even as larger and larger numbers come within the range of improved factorising techniques and faster machines, there will *always* be an infinity which lie beyond our reach.

The fact that the composite RSA129 was deliberately constructed as a product of two prime numbers is essential to the working of the cryptosystem. Prime numbers have become of prime importance.

In discussing Fermat's formula for generating primes, I mentioned two other mathematicians, Father Mersenne, a compatriot and contemporary of Fermat's, and Leonhard Euler, a Swiss mathematician who lived about a century after Fermat and who was a great admirer of the latter's work. Both Mersenne and Euler also had something to say about methods for generating prime numbers. Euler hit upon the formula

$$E(n) = n^2 - n + 41$$

when searching for ways to produce primes. $E(n)$ is called the *n-th Euler number* so that, for example, $E(1)$ is the first Euler number. Its value is obtained by substituting 1 for n in the expression $n^2 - n + 41$. So $E(1) = 41$ and the first Euler number is a prime. How about the second Euler number, $E(2)$? Well, $E(2) = 2^2 - 2 + 41 = 4 - 2 + 41 = 43$, so it is also a prime. Furthermore, $E(3) = 3^2 - 3 + 41 = 9 - 3 + 41 = 47$ is a prime, as is $E(4) = 53$. Incredibly, the first forty Euler numbers are all prime. But you would be sadly mistaken if, on the basis of these first forty cases, you were to believe or assert that this remarkable formula generates primes for every natural number n. Alas, and ironically,

$$E(41) = 1681 = 41 \times 41$$

is not prime. Neither is $E(42) = 1763 = 41 \times 43$, a product of twin primes. A gallant attempt, but one which unfortunately does not generate prime numbers exclusively. Maybe the quest for a formula which generates all the primes is a fruitless one?

Let us go back a century to Mersenne who studied the numbers generated by the formula

$$M(n) = 2^n - 1$$

when n is a natural number. It will come as no surprise to be told that these numbers are known today as *Mersenne numbers*. Let's calculate the first nine of these numbers and see what observations we might make:

$$M(1) = 2^1 - 1 = 2 - 1 = 1$$
$$M(2) = 2^2 - 1 = 4 - 1 = 3$$
$$M(3) = 2^3 - 1 = 8 - 1 = 7$$
$$M(4) = 2^4 - 1 = 16 - 1 = 15 = 3 \times 5$$
$$M(5) = 2^5 - 1 = 32 - 1 = 31$$

In Code

$$M(6) = 2^6 - 1 = 64 - 1 = 63 = 3^2 \times 7$$
$$M(7) = 2^7 - 1 = 128 - 1 = 127$$
$$M(8) = 2^8 - 1 = 256 - 1 = 255 = 3 \times 5 \times 17$$
$$M(9) = 2^9 - 1 = 512 - 1 = 511 = 7 \times 73$$

Now it is clear from these calculations that Mersenne could not have asserted that his formula is always going to produce prime numbers. It might appear from this small amount of numerical evidence that if n is composite then $M(n)$ is also composite, an assertion we can render succinctly in the form

$$n \text{ composite} \Rightarrow M(n) \text{ composite.}$$

(Recall that the symbol $\Rightarrow$ stands for 'implies that'.) This proposition is in fact true in general, and Mersenne would have known the little amount of algebra needed to prove it. I would love to show you how this is done but I do not want to 'blind you with science'. Dad showed us in class how to prove this result, and emphasised what a marvellous thing it is to be able to prove a general result. He also said that it is good to look at a result from different angles. For example, you could say that this result says that if you substitute a composite value for n into the formula $2^n - 1$ you *never* get a prime number. Check that $M(10) = 2^{10} - 1 = 1023$ is indeed composite. This is very easy. So there is no point substituting composite values for n if you want $M(n)$ to produce prime numbers. You must stick with prime values for n; it is *necessary* that n be prime for $M(n)$ to be prime. But is it always true that

$$n \text{ prime} \Rightarrow M(n) \text{ prime?}$$

In other words, is n being a prime *sufficient* to ensure that $M(n)$ is also a prime? Wouldn't it be great if this were true in general? The small amount of evidence available from the above calculations shows that when the prime values 2, 3, 5 and 7 are substituted in turn for n into the formula for $M(n)$, the resulting Mersenne numbers are also prime. But as we know from our recent discussion of Euler's formula, the truth of a proposition for a finite number of cases does not prove the result in general. So let's experiment a little more. I like this simple playful aspect of number theory where you can explore by calculating. Of course using a computer gives you vastly more scope, but sometimes it distracts from thinking. Anyway, substituting the next prime 11 for n gives $M(11) = 2^{11} - 1 = 2047$. Fingers crossed in the hope that this is a prime number. Test it with the trial division algorithm. Since $\sqrt{2047} = 45 \cdot 243...$, we need to divide 2047 in turn by the primes which are less than 45. If none of these 13 primes divides into 2047, then it is a prime, but if one of them does then it is a composite number. Unfortunately, 2047 is not a prime. I'm going to leave you to find its smallest prime factor. It will involve a small amount of calculation but finding the answer may help you appreciate how much time and effort the mathematicians of the sixteenth and seventeenth centuries expended on similar calculations. They were rewarded by discovering some amazing truths about numbers. So the proposition n prime $\Rightarrow M(n)$ prime is not true in general. Although it is necessary for the number n to be prime for $M(n)$ to be also prime, sadly it is not sufficient to ensure that $M(n)$ is prime.

A single 'ugly fact' has destroyed at one stroke a beautiful theory. This instance, where $2^{11} - 1$ is composite though 11 is a prime, is termed a *counter-example* to the general proposition. For a general proposition to be true, *every* single case must be true, which is a very stringent requirement: it takes only a single counter-example to make a proposition untrue in general. A generally true proposition is something to be admired.

If you substitute further prime numbers for n in Mersenne's formula, the resulting Mersenne numbers become very large and require much testing to see whether they are prime. Despite this, Mersenne asserted than $2^n - 1$ is prime for the prime values $n = 2$, 3, 5, 7, 13, 17, 19, 31, 67, 127 and 257, and *for no other primes* less than 257. He wasn't entirely right. The first eight of these values do give prime Mersenne numbers, but the 21-digit $M(67)$ is composite, a fact first discovered by the American mathematician Frank Cole. After two years of using his leisure time on Sundays, he factorised

$2^{67} - 1$. In 1903 he gave a completely silent 'lecture' which consisted of two calculations. He first worked out $2^{67} - 1$ to be 47573952589676412927. Then he multiplied 193707721 by 761838257287 and got the same result. Having shown that $M(67)$ is composite he then sat down to a standing ovation. Think of it – over two hundred days of calculations to factorise a 21-digit number. When I asked the wonderfully powerful mathematical package *Mathematica* to write out the 21 decimal digits of $M(67)$ it did so in the blink of an eye, and when I asked it to factorise this number it found the two prime factors in 1·792 seconds.

When I asked *Mathematica* if $M(127)$ is a prime, it returned the answer 'true' in less than half a second. However, when I asked it to factorise the 78-digit number $M(257)$, which is known to be a composite number, I got no immediate response other than an indication that the program was 'running'. It was still working away hours later. I eventually abandoned ship, but Dad put a faster computer to work on the same calculation beginning one Wednesday at 13.00. The 78-digit number was still not factorised almost a week later: at 8.30 the following Tuesday morning the 'running' message was still on the screen, indicating that the computer was still searching. The number $M(257)$ is known, since 1979, to be a product of three primes, the smallest of which is 535006138814359. Mersenne missed some numbers. Although the primes 61, 89 and 107 do not appear in his list, the numbers $M(61)$, $M(89)$ and $M(107)$ are in fact primes.

How was Mersenne able to make the claims he did in a time when, as far as we know, the art of factorising numbers was in its infancy? Near the end of the nineteenth century, the French mathematician Édouard Lucas found an efficient way of testing whether or not a Mersenne number is prime. This test, which was further refined by D.N. Lehmer in the twentieth century, is now known as the Lucas–Lehmer test. Because of its efficiency, searches to reveal a prime larger than the largest currently known are often confined to using this superfast test on Mersenne numbers. The search for larger and larger prime numbers is something of a hobby with many. I can remember Dad saying in January 1998 that he had read on the Internet of how a 19-year-old named Ronald Clarkson became one of the many thousands of members of GIMPS (Great Internet Mersenne Prime Search). This group of amateurs use their computers' 'idle time' and software written (by mathematician George Woltman) specifically for the purpose of searching for large primes among the Mersenne numbers. Ronald was rewarded when after many days of toil his home computer found

$$M(3021377) = 2^{3021377} - 1$$

to be a prime number. This Mersenne number was the largest prime known until June 1999. Could you say how many digits are in its decimal representation? The answer is a staggering 909526. If the entire London *Times* were devoted to printing this prime number, it would be found lacking. It is truly amazing that such a gigantic number has no factors other than itself and 1. On 1 June 1999, another member of the GIMPS group, Nayan Hajratwala, became the first person to find a *megaprime*, a prime number with a million or more digits. He found

$$M(6972593) = 2^{6972593} - 1$$

to be prime. This number has 2098960 digits – a megaprime indeed.

I have described three unsuccessful attempts to find a formula which generates prime numbers exclusively. Is there a formula that can do this? Apparently Jones, Sato, Wada and Wiens have discovered a complicated formula (if you must know, a polynomial of degree 25 in 26 variables) whose positive values are exactly *all* the prime numbers. I know nothing about it, but it is absolutely fascinating that such a formula exists. I'm told that this formula can yield negative values also, such as -76 which is not a prime. But who cares, considering what it achieves?

In Code

How Many Prime Numbers Are There Less Than a Given Number?

This is an important question, and many exact answers are known. There are exactly 25 primes less than 100, exactly 168 less than 1000 and exactly 1229 less than 10000. There are 74448 primes less than 1 million, 999983 being the largest. As of January 2000, the best-known exact result is that there are exactly

2220819602560918840 primes less than 1000000000000000000000

However, in general, given a natural number n, it is not known exactly how many primes are less than or equal to n. If you study the random way in which the primes make their appearance as you proceed along the natural numbers, you may not find it very surprising that an exact formula still eludes mathematicians. However, what is surprising is that one can estimate how many primes there are below each natural number. This famous result, known as the prime number theorem (PNT), was conjectured by mathematicians such as Carl Friedrich Gauss and Adrien Marie Legendre around 1800, based on their studies of prime number tables, and was not proved until 1896.

This theorem, for example, estimates the number of primes less than 1 million at 72382, which is not a bad approximation to the exact value of 74448. Sometimes we can get by well enough with rough estimates. We can never hope to know population sizes, newspaper circulations or programme ratings exactly, and are happy enough with estimates. We shall have occasion to use the PNT later.

Beginning the First Project

Soon after the Mathematical Excursions evening course began, in October 1997, one of the science teachers at my school, Seán Foley, started to look for students who would be willing to do a project for the Young Scientist Competition. This annual competition is held in early January in Dublin. Almost everybody in the country knows about it and each year there are hundreds of projects on display in the large hall at the Royal Dublin Society building. It began in 1964 and was sponsored by Aer Lingus, our national airline, until 1997, when Esat Telecom took it under its wing. The competition is now known as the Esat Young Scientist & Technology Exhibition. It was set up to encourage young people to become more involved in the sciences. It's a great idea, particularly if you are really interested in something, because you can investigate to your heart's content and do as much work as you want, knowing that you have the opportunity to present your ideas and the results of your labours in public. You may enter either with an individual project or, as part of a team of at most three, with a group project.

Mr Foley, who had brought students to this competition for a number of years, told us that we'd find it very exciting and gain great experience by displaying and explaining our projects to judges and the general public. We would also have a tremendous time meeting and talking with the other participants. He added that there was great fun to be had at the social events organised for the evenings and that we'd get to stay at Jury's Hotel for a very little because the Parents Association would pick up the rest of the tab. This all sounded very interesting – the only trouble was I didn't have any idea for a suitable topic. I loved doing projects at school in subjects like geography and history. I would try to find an unusual topic and include everything I could. As one teacher commented "You left no stone unturned" and put a lot of effort into the writing. But this was really no more than gathering and marshalling information in an attractive way (in fact organising – which I love; I'm not as good at keeping organised though). I was conscious of this fact and so I was a little unsure about undertaking a science project with a practical element in it.

Still, I knew it would be worth doing something just for the *craic*, as we say, to be had up in Dublin for five days. It was an ideal opportunity as I was in my Transition year with a lot of time which I could call my own. But what could I work on? One evening, as

In Code

Dad was driving us both to the evening class, I asked him if he had any ideas for a project for the competition. He knew about it because when he was at school many moons ago a student one year ahead of him had won a prize and became overnight one of the school's heroes. He said he hadn't any ideas, and asked, "Don't you have to carry out experimental investigations, gather data and draw conclusions?" I explained some of the types of project that had been submitted in more recent contests which Mr Foley had described to us when he was trying to sell the idea of entering the competition.

Then Dad said, after many "I don't knows" and as many hums and haws, "Maybe you could do something on cryptography, perhaps discuss some of the ideas, and for 'the bells and whistles end' do some programming. You could show messages being scrambled (enciphered or encrypted) to disguise them, and then unscrambled (deciphered or decrypted) by the receiver to recover the original message." He thought that it might be a good idea to have all this happening between two PCs. We talked a little about the fact that most people don't know anything about public key cryptography, which dates from 1976, and they might find the subject very interesting, particularly if I could show that these revolutionary ideas are of some practical importance. Hmm, maybe. By this time the evening class had covered a good deal of number theory and we were discussing cryptography, so if I did decide to take the plunge I'd have an extra reason to pay attention. I had also heard Dad rave about this mathematical package called *Mathematica* which he made out to be the cat's pyjamas, so it would be an opportunity to learn what this "wonderful piece of software" could do. I had some inkling that I would really love programming.

On the downside, I knew there had been some mathematical projects entered in previous competitions but I believed they'd been few and far between. I had some notion that the format for competition entry was not ideally suited to abstract projects, and more suited to ones involving experimental or field work, which seemed quite natural. Even so, there *is* a category named 'Mathematics, Physics and Chemistry', and after all I'd be presenting the programming of the mathematics as the practical element. Why not give it a shot?

That's how I got started on what I now call my first project, which I simply entitled 'Cryptography – The Science of Secrecy'. My plan was to present the terminology and notions by using as examples some of the simpler classical cryptosystems, beginning with the Caesar cipher. This system is very easy to describe and understand, and is ideal for introducing all the key terms. I would then present the fascinating ideas of public key cryptography, culminating with a description of the celebrated RSA system. All this would be accompanied by programs showing cryptosystems in action. Later I made a wheel to illustrate the Caesar cipher. Just making it was fun. The wheel looked great all prettied up, and it proved to be a big hit because it illustrates certain ideas which everyone can understand.

I knew there would be a lot of work to be done, but as usual I thought I could leave everything to the last minute, maybe a fortnight or so before the competition. I like working under pressure, but Dad encouraged me to get cracking as soon as possible. "It'll take time to assimilate the concepts, to let them mature and become clear in your mind. Anyway, you are almost sure to run into all sorts of difficulties at the programming end when you try to implement the mathematics. Projects don't have to be hectic affairs; better if you give yourself plenty of time and that you take your time." I knew he was right.

He was dead right about the programming. Near the end, when it came to writing up my report, I realised just how much work is involved in trying to present ideas clearly and simply without being overly technical. It is difficult trying to be crystal clear but well worth the effort if you succeed. I was to learn this lesson most emphatically when writing programs: you must know exactly what you want to achieve and write the code accordingly, otherwise it won't do what you hope it will and you end up tearing the hair out of your head. When you have to explain things clearly you really have to think from the bottom up. Wondering "How am I going to explain this or that to a lay person?" and asking "Well, what is really involved" are important. Dad has some quote (he always has!) from a French mathematician of the nineteenth century which goes, "A mathematical theory is not to be considered complete until you have made it so clear that you can explain it to the first man whom you meet on the street." This is a pretty tall order and it may not always be achievable. More comforting is something I heard attributed to Einstein, which I paraphrase as, "You should strive to make things as simple as possible but no simpler." Now that's a little more realistic, as well as being a witty warning against oversimplification.

If you really want to learn something, learn it with a view to explaining it to somebody else. I found Mom to be the best person on whom to test this theory. She thinks slowly and carefully and will let you get away with absolutely nothing. At times you'd think her stupid until you'd realise that you were the stupid one for expecting her to grasp some idea without having supplied vital facts. So I learned to order my thoughts. She asked tough questions which always sounded simple but were right to the point. On a trip to Dublin in the car I was trying, by way of practice, to explain some cryptographic ideas to her. I'd talk for a while and then she'd ask a question. Dad, who was snoozing in the front passenger seat, would pipe up every now and then with "That's a great question." I felt a bit small on hearing this because perhaps I hadn't asked myself that question. But Dad didn't mean to make me feel this way, though when it comes to our explaining things he doesn't spare our feelings if he thinks we're waffling. He often advises, "Speak clearly and simply. Tell a person what you know and come clean when you don't know something. Don't bluff." I know his general attitude is that you should ask simple natural questions of yourself, put yourself in the other fellow's shoes and try to see his difficulties. At one point while I was explaining to Mom something called the RSA signature scheme (of which I'll talk later), she went, "Let me get this clear. You are saying that you actually decrypt first and then encrypt." I'll always remember that remark. It was right on the nail, and I could see her difficulty – how could you be decrypting ordinary text (plaintext) or why would you be doing it? I had to think for a while before elaborating with an explanation. This explaining business really kept you on your toes. Dad loved it all, and again said, "They're great questions, Mom." At this Michael, who by this time was completely frustrated at being cooped up in a car listening to all this crazy talk, saw his opportunity and struck: "Dad thinks every question is a great question! 'What time is it?' is a great question in Dad's mind." There was general laughter and no more cryptographic talk. Have a break. Enjoy the scenery – it was (probably) raining.

Learning the Relevant Mathematics

The project required that I learn number theory (really learn it), the necessary cryptographic ideas, and how to program in *Mathematica* so as to implement and illustrate the cryptographic schemes. The first thing I realised about learning mathematics was that there is a hell of a difference between, on the one hand, listening to maths being talked about by somebody else and thinking that you are understanding, and, on the other, thinking about maths and under-standing it yourself and talking about it to somebody else.

In the beginning I was inclined to accept mathematical facts in the same way that I accept geographical ones. I felt that I grasped concepts fairly quickly, but I now know that I didn't ask why things are the way they are often enough, as a true scientist should. As a result I found that sometimes I didn't appreciate how important a certain detail might be. Knowing that Paris is the capital of France is something you don't think much more about, but to know what Fermat's Little Theorem is saying requires thought. You really have to tease out under what conditions the result is true, and explore it to get to know what exactly is being asserted. This was all a little intimidating at first but I knew I could call on Dad if it got too much for me. He's only too willing to talk maths all day long. I was very lucky in that I quickly found programming to be a great help in learning some of the mathematics. Many results in number theory are ideally suited to being programmed, and the mere act of trying to write a few instructions in sequence in order to display some examples of a general result helped me to learn this type of mathematics in an easy and natural way. I even got to appreciate some of those details that many often find fussy or annoying in mathematical results. From my perspective, overlooking some significant little detail, while frustrating, was nothing to get too het up about. It was like someone wondering why the car won't start only to find that the reason is as simple as having forgotten to put petrol in the tank. Because of this I became less inclined to think, "Why does this result have to be so restrictive in what it says?" I could see the sense of the details and so I learned to be tolerant.

As planned, I used the mathematical software package *Mathematica* to implement the cryptographic schemes. With *Mathematica* you can do computations just like a calculator, but with much larger numbers. More importantly, you can also use it to write programs. That was something I was going to have to learn. For me the initial thrill was simply to see how this package deals with huge numbers with such speed. I just love to calculate – even the simplest of calculations (getting it to print the first 100 digits of π or expand 3^{76} so that I could see the numbers roll across the screen). It is spectacular to think how long it would take to do these by hand. Contrast the time people spent working out successive digits of π (and making up rhymes so that they could remember them) with the microseconds *Mathematica* takes to reel off the first thousand digits of this number. Learning simple commands such as **PrimeQ[ ]** or **FactorInteger[ ]** which aren't on a calculator made me feel powerful, though in reality I wasn't doing anything. Typing **PrimeQ[2^{32} + 1]** and getting the output **False** as soon as the command was entered was wonderful, especially when I remembered that Fermat believed this number to be prime. Typing **FactorInteger[2^{32} + 1]** to get in the blink of an eye the factors 641 and 6700417 was even more exciting.

After much time spent playing with the many different commands, some of which I knew I would never need, I decided it was time to take my first baby steps in programming. One of the first tasks I set myself was to go back through my number theory notes and search out simple numerical statements which would involve huge amounts of labour for a human to illustrate by examples, but which would be no bother for a computer. So I began my programming by writing short sequences of instructions to carry out the necessary calculations. For example, I wrote code to make out lists of the Fermat, Euler and Mersenne numbers along with their factorisations. This is very straightforward, and the results are printed in a matter of seconds. Then I tried to fine-tune the code a little to get more information, such as which ones are prime and which are not. This is a little more challenging. I found that as I worked away, improving here and there, other little refinements would suggest themselves. It wasn't always easy to tell the computer how to carry them out. I acquired a great respect for how versatile the human brain is.

When I grew in confidence I started to learn how to turn ordinary text (plaintext) into scrambled text (ciphertext), a process known as *enciphering*. This wasn't too hard, but I did spend a lot of time reading the relevant sections of the 1500-page manual, all the while having to fight the temptation to explore some of the wonderful commands I came across as I leafed through this massive tome. Eventually I got to the stage where I could turn chunks of plaintext into huge numbers, which I then turned into different huge numbers, which then got converted into blocks of ciphertext. The next stage was to reverse the process, which is called *deciphering*. Although the two processes are the same mathematically, it was for me much more of a test, because I may not have been doing the enciphering properly. So I had my fingers crossed that all would work with the reversing process, nervously wondering, "Will the original plaintext reappear?" Relief and joy when it did. I knew it should happen, but it was still such an ease to see the correct plaintext pop up on the screen, verifying that the code, however primitive it might be, was doing its job.

Often one of those annoying little bugs would have me tracking it for hours, forcing me to break up entire sections of code, going down through it step by step to pinpoint exactly where the little pest was hiding and how was it managing to mess up what otherwise seemed a perfectly logical program. Line by line I'd dissect and examine code. Yes, this is working, so is that. Now what is happening here? Try this – no good. Whoops – I've made it worse. "Erase and rewind 'cause I'm a changin' my mind", as the song says. Maybe it is this – Noooo! (followed by foul language). OK, relax! Don't be in such a rush. Think. Think. What am I asking the program to do? Yes. Is that what I meant it to do? Oops, not quite! Ah yes, it is doing that but I wanted it to do this. Gotcha!

3 . What Matters Is What's Left Over

*I*f you have survived all the talk about prime numbers and didn't find the going too hard, you'll have no trouble reading what's in this chapter. Don't worry if all the mathematical details are not jumping off the page at you, just skim to get the general picture. If, however, you've already found the maths a little too heavy, you are probably not reading these lines but have gone on to Chapter 5, where the wonderful concepts of modern cryptography can be gleaned without knowledge of their mathematical underpinning.

This chapter has two aims. The first is to introduce a little notation and terminology, which more than likely will be new to you. This is done by posing some puzzle-like problems which are simple and involve arithmetic calculations that will be familiar to most. I show you a little trick which will make your friends believe you have magician-like mathematical capabilities. Interested?

Secondly, by describing the Caesar cipher in detail I reinforce the cryptographic language I have already used in the last chapter, and show you some of the nuts and bolts of enciphering and deciphering text. What I love about Caesar's system is that it's simple and that it allows so many of the main concepts and terminology of cryptography to be explained naturally. I hope you'll begin to see why I became so interested in the subject.

In Code

A hundred days from now

Which day of the week will it be 100 days from now if today is Sunday?

One way of solving this problem is to use a calculator to get that

$$\frac{100}{7} = 14 \cdot 285714\ldots$$

Why divide 100 by 7? Because there are 7 days in a week. Since the result of our calculation is not an exact integer we conclude that 100 days contains 14 full weeks with a few days to spare. To calculate the number of days left over or remaining we work out that these 14 weeks will take $14 \times 7 = 98$ days to elapse. This done, we subtract the result of this calculation, 98, from the total number of days, 100, to get 2 as the number of days remaining. These two calculations can be combined:

$$100 - (14 \times 7) = 100 - 98 = 2$$

Equivalently,

$$100 = 14 \times 7 + 2$$

– a form which shows 100 as being made up of 14 multiples of 7 and a remainder of 2.

Perhaps the 'short division'

$$7\overline{)100} \atop 14 + 2$$

taught in junior school reveals more quickly that $100 = 14 \times 7 + 2$.

In the language of weeks and days, $100 = 14 \times 7 + 2$ shows that 100 days consists of 14 full weeks and 2 extra days. So if today is Sunday then it will be a Tuesday in 100 days' time, because after

14 full weeks it will be a Sunday again and the 2 extra days bring the day of the week to Tuesday.

If we ask similar questions – such as which day of the week it will be in a thousand days' time or in a million days' time – then we will need to do new calculations like the one above in order to answer them. But throughout we shall always be dividing by the number 7 because it measures the number of days in a week. When we are dealing with a positive divisor which remains constant from problem to problem, it is called the *modulus*; a term which is a first cousin of a Latin word for 'measure'. If we are dealing with problems relating to clock times, the modulus will either be 12 or 24, while if we are dealing with problems involving angles the underlying modulus will be 360.

In the above calculation what really matters is the number 2 which is left over after 7 is subtracted 14 times from 100. It is this remainder 2 which points to the day of the week. In the notation of mathematics we can write

$$100 \bmod 7 = 2$$

to indicate that 2 is the remainder when 100 is divided by the fixed number, or modulus, 7.

Here is a charming story from Richard Guy, quoted in *Lure of the Integers* by Joe Roberts, which has some connection with our discussion. In Guy's words:

> There used to be an admission examination, the '11-plus', to British secondary schools. A question that was asked on one occasion was "Take 7 from 93 as many times as you can." One child answered, "I get 86 every time." I hope she got her place!

Did the examiners expect the students to know that, in our 'mod' notation, $93 \bmod 7 = 2$ (which is just a very compact way of saying that when 7 is taken from 93 as many times as possible the number 2 remains), or did they want them to say that you can take 7 from 93 thirteen times?

In Code

When working 'with respect to' the modulus 7 there can be only seven possible remainders, namely 0, 1, 2, 3, 4, 5 or 6. It is useful to imagine these numbers written on a clock face in the way the numbers 1 to 12 ordinarily appear. Let the number 0 be at the top (where 12 is on the ordinary clock), and let the other six numerals be placed in order at equally spaced intervals around the perimeter of the clock. Call this clock a week-day clock, and imagine the different days of the week written under the seven numerals in small letters, with Sunday appearing below the 0 so that Saturday appears beneath the 6, which is to the left of the 0. If you wish you may also imagine that this clock has a single hand pivoted at the centre of its face and pointing to the current day, only moving at the stroke of midnight.

If the hand of this clock points at the numeral 0 then today is Sunday. In 100 days' time the clock's hand will have made fourteen full rotations in the clockwise direction, and moved on a further two days, and so will point at the numeral 2. Hence 100 days from now it will be a Tuesday.

Let's use this clock to figure out which day of the week it was 100 days ago if today is Sunday. To go backwards in time, imagine the hand of the clock moving anticlockwise. Starting at 0, fourteen full rotations in the anticlockwise direction brings it back to 0. Continuing a further two days will bring it to the numeral 5, so if today is Sunday then it was a Friday 100 days ago.

Since we use 100 for the purpose of calculating which day it will be a hundred days into the future, we use -100 (minus 100) to calculate one hundred days into the past. If the 'mod' operation is to indicate that 100 days ago it was a Friday, it must be that $-100 \bmod 7 = 5$. This allows the day of the week to be read directly.

You might argue, since $-100 = (-14) \times 7 + (-2)$, that $-100 \bmod 7$ should be -2, and you might reinforce your point by adding that -2 indicates the day of the week just as effectively as 5 does. The -2 says "Go back two days from 0 (which represents Sunday) to arrive at Friday." However, there are no negative numbers on the clock face.

The convention with the mod operation is that every number,

64

be it a positive or a negative number or 0, when divided by the modulus leaves as a remainder either 0 or one of the positive numbers less than the modulus. In this way the answer always comes out as a number on the clock face.

From this viewpoint, -12 leaves a remainder of 2 when divided by 7. Why? Because $-12 = (-2) \times 7 + 2$. Thus $-12 \bmod 7 = 2$, a result which is easily understood by moving in the anticlockwise direction around the week-day clock. Note that $-2 \times 7 + 2$ can be interpreted as saying, "Starting at 0, make two full anticlockwise rotations to arrive at 0 again, and then go clockwise through 2 days."

Convince yourself that $-3 \bmod 7 = 4$ and $-13 \bmod 7 = 1$.

Here are a few more calculations involving the modulus 7:

$63 \bmod 7 = 0$	$8 \bmod 7 = 1$	$583 \bmod 7 = 2$
$647 \bmod 7 = 3$	$410 \bmod 7 = 4$	$691 \bmod 7 = 5$
$314 \bmod 7 = 6$	$4 \bmod 7 = 4$	$-8 \bmod 7 = 6$

Some explanations: $63 \bmod 7 = 0$ because $63 = 9 \times 7 + 0$, while $314 \bmod 7 = 6$ because $314 = 44 \times 7 + 6$. Furthermore, $4 \bmod 7 = 4$ because $4 = 0 \times 7 + 4$. This says that 7 goes into 4 zero times with a remainder of 4. In terms of the week-day clock, the hand has moved from 0, through 4 days, and now points at 4. Using the same clock, $-8 \bmod 7 = 6$, because starting from 0, the negative number -8 indicates a full anticlockwise rotation followed by a further rotation through one day in the same direction to arrive at 6. Alternatively, think of it as $-8 = -2 \times 7 + 6$ so that $-8 \bmod 7 = 6$.

When a number is divided by 7, it can leave one and only one of the remainders 0, 1, 2, 3, 4, 5 or 6. Should it leave the remainder 0 when divided by 7, as 63 does, then the number is divisible by 7. If the number leaves any of the other remainders when divided by 7, then that number is not divisible by 7.

Here are some more examples with respect to different moduli:

In Code

$$800 \bmod 360 = 80 \qquad 70 \bmod 11 = 4 \qquad 8678 \bmod 24 = 14$$

The first result could be interpreted as saying that an angle of 800°
is the same as angle of 80°, while the second result might tell us that
if soccer teams are made up from 70 players then exactly 4 will be
left on the touchline. The final result might inform us that if it is
now four o'clock in the afternoon, then in 8678 hours it will be six
o'clock in the morning.

A Party Trick

Here is a nice party trick perhaps best done with a calculator. It is
based on a mathematical result exotically named the *Chinese
remainder theorem*. This result has many important (practical)
applications besides the one to be described.

*If someone tells me the three numbers remaining when she divides her
age by 3, 5 and 7 respectively then I can work out her age.*

Here's how it is done. Suppose the person in question is aged a
years. It is assumed that a is a natural number less than 105 (a
restriction likely to be satisfied by most party-goers). The three
remainders are $a \bmod 3$, $a \bmod 5$ and $a \bmod 7$. Suppose they work
out to be x, y and z, respectively. Then, mysteriously (don't expect to
understand why),

$$a = (70x + 21y + 15z) \bmod 105$$

This formula always works. Suppose, for example, that you, the
reader, are aged seventeen. Then $a = 17$ with

$$a \bmod 3 = 17 \bmod 3 = 2$$
$$a \bmod 5 = 17 \bmod 5 = 2$$
$$a \bmod 7 = 17 \bmod 7 = 3$$

Thus the three remainders which you give me are 2, 2 and 3, respectively. These are all I need to find your age. I set $x = 2$, $y = 2$ and $z = 3$ and, if necessary, with the aid of a calculator, I compute

$$70x + 21y + 15z = 70 \times 2 + 21 \times 2 + 15 \times 3$$
$$= 140 + 42 + 45$$
$$= 227$$

This done, I work out that $227 = 2 \times 105 + 17$ and so get $a = 227 \bmod 105 = 17$. Then I announce that you are seventeen years of age.

You can take it on trust that no other natural number less than 105 leaves this set of three remainders. Each natural number less than 105 has a unique triple of remainders which identify it. (Observe that $3 \times 5 \times 7 = 105$.)

If you really want to impress, train yourself to do all the arithmetic in your head. Some ages involve less mental calculation than others.

But can the remainders of numbers upon division by 7 or any other modulus be worked out *without* first determining how often the modulus goes into the number? Amazingly, yes. In some cases, even for colossal numbers, almost effortlessly. There is a special 'arithmetic of remainders' introduced by a young German mathematician around 1800 of which I hope to give you a glimpse. It allows us to calculate remainders without having to do divisions. This is the arithmetic used in cryptography and is explained in the next chapter. But the 'mod' notation is all that is needed to describe some simple classical cryptosystems.

Before I begin to show how the 'mod' notation is used as an aid in describing cryptosystems, I should say just a little about the central aim of cryptography and why it is used, although I know that most readers will already have a pretty good idea about the nature and aims of this science of secrecy.

Basically, cryptography is about keeping nosey parkers and/or more sinister characters with evil intentions from reading private messages intended for other people. Unfortunately, this is the way of

In Code

the world, so great pains must be taken to turn these messages into gobbledygook before sending them to their destination. Then, should the aforementioned disreputable characters manage to intercept, or eavesdrop, or simply get a glimpse of the disguised message by some clever but illegitimate means, they will not immediately be able to make any sense of what they read. If you are knowledgeable enough you can encipher the message so that they will never be able to decipher it in a realistic amount of time, no matter how ingenious they may be and how unlimited their resources. That's about it in a nutshell.

In my first project report, I wrote a little more formally:

As long as there are creatures endowed with language there will be the desire for confidential communication – messages intended for a limited audience. Governments, companies and individuals have a need to send messages in such a way that only the intended recipient is able to read them. Generals send battle orders, banks wire fund transfers and individuals make purchases using credit cards.

I continued by saying that the central problem of cryptography is:

How can a message be transmitted secretly to its intended recipient so that no unauthorised person obtains knowledge of its content?

Cryptography is the study of methods of sending messages in disguised form so that only those for whom they are intended can remove the mask and read their contents. In former times it was used mainly by the military and diplomatic services, but with the advent of electronic communication it is increasingly being used by financial institutions to ensure privacy in transactions between client and customer.

The Caesar Cipher

One of the first military figures to encipher messages was Julius

Caesar. He used the simple idea of substituting different letters of the alphabet for the actual letters of the message, or plaintext. This he did in a systematic fashion by *shifting* the alphabet forward three places so that a was enciphered as d, b as e and so on, the three letters x, y and z being 'wrapped around' and enciphered as a, b and c, respectively. This can be done efficiently by arranging the ciphertext alphabet beneath the plaintext alphabet as follows:

plaintext	a	b	c	d	e	f	g	...	v	w	x	y	z
ciphertext	d	e	f	g	h	i	j	...	y	z	a	b	c

Thus, without too much effort, he could encipher this message is top secret as **wklvphvvdjhlvwrsvhfuhw**. Here the blank spaces occurring in the ordinary plaintext have been suppressed. To better display the enciphering/deciphering relationship we write

this message is top secret → **wklvphvvdjhlvwrsvhfuhw**

The arrow indicates that the plaintext message transforms into the ciphertext cipher. The word 'cipher' in this context means a secret message, whereas in Caesar's cipher it means a method of writing messages in secret.

The Caesar cipher is an example of a *character* or *monographic substitution cipher* since it enciphers by substituting single (mono) letters (characters) for other single letters.

To decipher the received cipher the recipient need only interchange the roles of the two alphabets, or if preferred to shift back three characters, forming the following table:

ciphertext	d	e	f	g	h	i	j	...	y	z	a	b	c
plaintext	a	b	c	d	e	f	g	...	v	w	x	y	z

Then

wklvlvkrzzhghflskhu → thisishowwedecipher

which is easily seen to be 'this is how we decipher'. We could write

thisishowwedecipher ← **wklvlvkrzzhghflskhu**

and so keep the ciphertext on the right. Here the arrow pointing from right to left indicates that decipherment, as opposed to encipherment, has taken place.

Decipher **wubdjdlq** assuming it has been enciphered using the system just described.

Occasionally a word becomes another recognisable English word when it is enciphered. A good example of this is the word 'cold'. Encipher it and see.

Clearly one can use shifts other than 3. 'Hal', the name of the computer in Arthur C. Clarke's *2001: A Space Odyssey*, was chosen because it is obtained from 'IBM' by a forward shift of 25 – or, equivalently and much more conveniently, by a backward shift of 1. Of course, the longer a word, the less likely it is to be enciphered as another English word. One of the longest of such words in English is 'abjurer'. In a 13-shift cipher it becomes 'nowhere'. You might like to determine what happens to 'pecan' in a 4-shift cipher or to 'sleep' in a 9-shift cipher.

There is no need to have two separate tables like the ones I used for illustrative purposes. One will do. To encipher read the first table from top to bottom, while to decipher read it from bottom to top. An attractive alternative is to make a Caesar wheel from two cardboard discs, one slightly larger than the other. Place the smaller one on top of the larger one with their centres superimposed, and mark off 26 even (very even!) sectors by lines extending from the centre to the edge of the larger disc. Mark the letters of the alphabet (in order) in these sectors near the edges of each disc. Pin the discs together at their centres so that they are free to spin independently. It is now easy to set up any of the 26 possible letter shifts. For a 5-shift simply turn the inner disc or wheel so that its *f* is beneath the *a* on the outer disc. All the other letters will be aligned correctly.

The Caesar cipher is a cryptosystem which can be thought of as applying solely to alphabetic characters. It can be implemented using tables or wheels, or even on a computer, *without* ever having to use numbers. However, it is best, for at least two reasons, if at their core cryptosystems use numbers. The first reason is that computers are ideally suited to handling numbers, even huge ones, with great speed. The second is that there is a large body of mathematical functions available which can transform numbers into other numbers in complicated ways. This makes it possible to design secure but efficient systems. No doubt very secure systems can be designed which make no use of numbers, but can they function efficiently? There is no point in having the instruction "sell shares at 140" cloaked in impenetrable secrecy if the share price has dropped through the floor by the time the message is deciphered.

Numbers for Letters

The table

a	b	c	d	e	f	g	h	i	...	v	w	x	y	z
0	1	2	3	4	5	6	7	8	...	21	22	23	24	25

assigns to each of the 26 (lower-case) letters of the alphabet a unique whole number between 0 and 25. These numbers are called the *numerical equivalents* of the letters. The letter e has the numerical equivalent 4. The reason why the letters of the alphabet are assigned the numbers 0 to 25 as opposed to 1 to 26 will become clear very soon. It will also become clear that the letters in the top row of the table are sometimes used as plaintext characters and sometimes as ciphertext characters.

Thinking in terms of the numbers instead of the letters, what does the Caesar cipher described earlier do? Add 3 to each number? True most of the time, but not always because of the 'wrap around' at the end of the alphabet. Adding 3 to the number 4 gives the number 7. Since 4 is the numerical equivalent of the letter e, and 7 is the numerical equivalent of the letter h, e gets enciphered as h which is correct. However, simply adding 3 to 24, which is the

In Code

numerical equivalent of y, will not encipher this letter correctly as 27 is not a numerical equivalent of any character.

So how to iron out this wrinkle? What to do with those numbers that exceed 25? Since y is supposed to encipher to **b**, which has numerical equivalent 1, the number 27 must be converted to a 1. Can you see how to turn 27 into 1?

Remember the 'mod' notation? Isn't $27 \bmod 26 = 1$? Numbers which exceed 25 when 'reduced by the size of the alphabet' (which is 26 in this case) will become the correct numerical equivalents of the corresponding ciphertext characters. The number 26 becomes 0, while 27 becomes 1, and 28 becomes 2. If 27 is regarded as 1, then the letter y is enciphered correctly as **b**.

Instead of saying "add 3 to each numerical equivalent", the instruction is "add 3 to each numerical equivalent reducing by 26 any number larger than 25". The arithmetic which does this correctly is arithmetic with respect to the modulus 26. The phrase 'with respect the modulus' is usually abbreviated 'modulo' so, with this new terminology, the correct arithmetic is *arithmetic modulo 26*. When working modulo 26 the only possible remainders are numbers in the range 0 to 25. It is for this reason that the letters of the alphabet are assigned the numbers 0 to 25 rather than 1 to 26 or some other range.

However, it is sometimes convenient to allow numbers, even negative ones, outside the range 0 to 25 to appear in calculations when working modulo 26, as their use often makes things simpler. You'll see some examples later. If required, it is always possible to use a number between 0 and 25 which performs the same function.

The Enciphering and Deciphering Formulae

To describe concisely the procedure for the Caesar cipher with a shift of 3, it helps to let P stand for the numerical equivalent of a typical plaintext character, and C stand for the numerical equivalent of the corresponding ciphertext character. Then the equation

What Matters Is What's Left Over

$$C = (P + 3) \bmod 26$$

gives the general encipherment rule. Isn't this a simple and a practical use of the mod notation?

It is important to bear in mind that though P and C are written as letters, they are in fact *numbers*. The P-number of the letter x is 23, so the corresponding C-number is

$$C = (23 + 3) \bmod 26 = 26 \bmod 26 = 0$$

Since 0 is the numerical equivalent of **a**, this scheme gives the correct encipherment x → **a**.

When I eventually knuckled down to programming, one of my first tasks was to get this end of the Caesar system working. It wasn't that hard to do, but I had to learn how to split a piece of text into single characters, assign each character its numerical equivalent, find the corresponding ciphertext numerical equivalents (the C-numbers) and then turn all these into single ciphertext characters. This last step can be omitted by simply leaving the plaintext enciphered as a string of numbers, but I preferred to show English text being enciphered into meaningless text. It was great fun learning the *Mathematica* commands to do all this, arranging them into a sequence of instructions and seeing chunks of ordinary English being transformed into an unreadable mess. I know now that a lot of the programming I did was fairly primitive, but just seeing it work was a real kick. To be sure that I was enciphering properly I had to convert the chaos of seemingly random ciphertext into the 'order' it once was.

So how to decipher with a Caesar system which uses a forward shift of 3? Clearly, *shift back* 3, taking care to wrap around when the need arises. So the decphering rule is described by

$$P = (C - 3) \bmod 26$$

To decipher the letter **b**, which has a C-number of 1, calculate

$$P = (1 - 3)\bmod 26 = -2\bmod 26 = 24$$

Since 24 is the numerical equivalent of y, the ciphertext character **b** deciphers as the plaintext character y, as it should.

Why is $-2\bmod 26 = 24$? On a clock face displaying the numbers 0 to 25 in the usual order, moving two steps anticlockwise from the number 0 brings us to the number 24. To confirm this result, think of a (backward) shift of -3 as a forward shift of 23. Then

$$P = (1 + 23)\bmod 26 = 24\bmod 26 = 24$$

as before.

Of course, Caesar didn't have to confine himself to a shift of 3. Because the lower-case alphabet has 26 letters he could have used any of the 26 different possible shifts of the alphabet, though a shift of 0 doesn't do any enciphering at all. If the letter s is used to stand for the size of a typical shift, then the formula

$$C = (P + s)\bmod 26$$

describes the enciphering rule for a Caesar cipher with forward shift s. In the original example above, $s = 3$.

It should be clear when 's' is 'itself' and when it's acting as a number. For example, for a Caesar cipher with a shift of 10 the letter s gets enciphered as **c**, as is easy to see. The numerical equivalent of the letter s is $P = 18$, while the size of the shift in the formula is $s = 10$. Thus

$$C = (18 + 10)\bmod 26 = 28\bmod 26 = 2$$

The C-number 2 is the numerical equivalent of the letter c.

Clearly, the formula

$$P = (C - s)\bmod 26$$

describes the deciphering rule corresponding to the enciphering rule for a general Caesar cipher with a forward shift of size s.

Keys

In the last century Jean Guillaume Hubert Victor François Alexandre Auguste Kerckhoffs von Nieuwenhof (1835–1903) enunciated **Kerckhoffs' principle**: The security of a cryptosystem must not depend on keeping the cryptographic algorithm secret. The security depends only on keeping the keys secret.

For the general Caesar cryptosystem described above, the number s representing the size of the forward shift employed is termed the *enciphering key*. If K_E is used as a shorthand for 'enciphering key', then for the general Caesar cipher,

$$K_E = s$$

The corresponding *deciphering key*, representing the size of the backward shift required to achieve deciphering, is the number $-s$. If K_D denotes 'deciphering key', then for the general Caesar cipher,

$$K_D = -s$$

Between them, K_E and K_D are termed the *keys* of a cryptosystem. The Caesar cipher based on a forward shift of 3 has keys $K_E = 3$ and $K_D = -3$.

In the context of the Caesar system, Kerckhoffs' principle states that the security of the system should not depend on Caesar's enemies' ignorance of his general method of secret writing. It is to be expected that eventually his system will become known to people other than those originally 'in the know'. From the very outset it is known to the generals with whom he uses it for private communication, and there is always the possibility that one or other of these generals will become an enemy at some stage. The security of the

In Code

system must depend on keeping both the enciphering and deciphering keys secret.

Cryptanalysis

In practice, a Caesar cipher could never be considered a secure cryptosystem. Keeping its keys secret is not enough. If it is known that it is being used, then it can be 'broken' or 'cracked' quite easily by analysing captured ciphertext. One approach checks all possible values of $-s$ until a decipherment results in readable plaintext. This form of attack searches through the set of all possible keys – what is called the *keyspace* – until the correct one is found. In this case it is feasible even by hand because the size of the keyspace is only 25.

Another approach to breaking this system is to use *frequency analysis* based on the table, which gives the percentage of occurrence of each of the letters of the alphabet in typical English plaintext.

Character	a	b	c	d	e	f	g	h	i	j	k
Relative frequency	7	1	3	4	13	3	2	3	8	<1	<1

l	m	n	o	p	q	r	s	t	u	v	w	x	y	z
4	3	8	7	3	<1	8	6	9	3	1	1	<1	2	<1

Calculate the frequencies of each of the ciphertext characters. If there is enough ciphertext available, then the ciphertext character with the highest frequency will normally correspond to the plaintext letter e, as this letter occurs the most frequently in English plaintext. The shift size s is then determined by calculating the number of steps necessary to transform e into the corresponding ciphertext character.

The science of breaking cryptosystems is known as *cryptanalysis*.

What Matters Is What's Left Over

Keeping Your Distance

By this stage you may be thinking that using numbers to represent letters is making everything more long-winded and creating an awful lot of complication where there seems to be no need for any. However, the numbers approach pays off when plaintext is enciphered in a more sophisticated way, in an effort to put more distance between a legitimate user and the ever-present enemy.

As a first step in designing a more complex cryptosystem, one might use a much larger 'alphabet', including both the ordinary lower-case and upper-case characters, along with the usual punctuation symbols. Often the alphabets used are of size 128 or 256 symbols. If n is the number of symbols used in the alphabet, then the enciphering and deciphering transformations for a cryptosystem based on a Caesar cipher with shift s are given by

$$C = (P + s) \bmod n \qquad P = (C - s) \bmod n$$

respectively. Now all arithmetic is done modulo n rather than modulo 26.

Even though the keyspace is much larger, this generalised Caesar system is still vulnerable to a computer search for s. A frequency analysis attack, on the other hand, requires much more preliminary statistical work to establish the relative frequencies of the occurrence of symbols from the larger plaintext alphabet.

What else can be done besides increasing the alphabet size? Why not try to improve on the Caesar system? This system essentially adds a fixed number s to each P-number and reduces the answer modulo n to get a natural number less than the modulus. How about multiplying instead of adding?

Let us experiment on the lower-case alphabet, so we are back to working modulo 26. In practice, the general modulus n would be much larger. Let's encrypt a typical P-number by multiplying it by 5, say. Then the enciphering rule says that

$$C = 5P \bmod 26$$

which is very simple.

The following array shows what happens to the twenty-six *P*-numbers 0 to 25 when each is enciphered according to this rule:

P	→	*C*		*P*	→	*C*
0	→	0		13	→	13
1	→	5		14	→	18
2	→	10		15	→	23
3	→	15		16	→	2
4	→	20		17	→	7
5	→	25		18	→	12
6	→	4		19	→	17
7	→	9		20	→	22
8	→	14		21	→	1
9	→	19		22	→	6
10	→	24		23	→	11
11	→	3		24	→	16
12	→	8		25	→	21

Before we begin enthusing about the two wonderful columns of *C*-numbers, let's make sure we understand how these numbers appear. For example, the *P*-number 22 becomes the *C*-number 6 because

$$5 \times 22 = 110 = 4 \times 26 + 6 \Rightarrow (5 \times 22) \bmod 26 = 6$$

Verify a few more; well, at least one more. The array shows that the set

$$\{0, 1, 2, 3, 4, 5, 6, 7, 8, 9, 10, 11, 12, 13, 14, 15, 16, 17, 18, 19, 20, 21, 22, 23, 24, 25\}$$

is transformed by the enciphering rule $C = 5P \bmod 26$ into the set

$$\{0, 5, 10, 15, 20, 25, 4, 9, 14, 19, 24, 3, 8, 13, 18, 23, 2, 7, 12, 17, 22, 1, 6, 11, 16, 21\}$$

What Matters Is What's Left Over

What's great about this is that *all* original twenty-six *P*-numbers reappear as *C*-numbers. This is significant because each *P*-number has a unique *C*-number – as it should – and, just as importantly, each *C*-number corresponds to a unique *P*-number. This kind of correspondence between the set of *P*-numbers and the set of *C*-numbers is very aptly described as a 'one-to-one' correspondence. (Later, we'll see that matters work out somewhat more disappointingly when we multiply by 4 instead of 5.) Whereas the Caesar encipherment rule *rotated* the twenty-six *P*-numbers, the current encipherment rule *permutes* these twenty-six *P*-numbers. Notice how nicely the numbers get jumbled by this enciphering process.

If the numbers in the above array are replaced by their corresponding letters, the plaintext alphabet

{a, b, c, d, e, f, g, h, i, j, k, l, m, n, o, p, q, r, s, t, u, v, w, x, y, z}

is seen to encipher into the ciphertext alphabet

{a, f, k, p, u, z, e, j, o, t, y, d, i, n, s, x, c, h, m, r, w, b, g, l, q, v}

Thus the following enciphering/deciphering table is obtained:

plaintext	a	b	c	d	e	f	g	h	i	...	v	w	x	y	z
ciphertext	a	f	k	p	u	z	e	j	o	...	b	g	l	q	v

This table, consisting of characters alone, could be used to carry out all the enciphering and deciphering without ever having to make any use of numbers. An example of encipherment is

evacuate immediately → ubakwaruoiiupoatudq

while an example of decipherment is

buy oil shares ← vekimxoratgo

In Code

Constant looking-up of a table can be very time-consuming, particularly when much larger alphabets are involved. Although it may not appear so yet, it is preferable to work as much as possible with numbers rather than characters. This being so, an interesting question now arises. What is the deciphering rule corresponding to the enciphering rule $C = 5P \bmod 26$? How do we go from a C-number, such as 22, back to the P-number that generated it? Consulting the above array of numbers and reading from right to left to find that the corresponding P-number is 20 is not considered to be legitimate because it involves 'table look-up'. What is required is a mathematical rule which, given a C-number, produces the corresponding P-number.

If it were ordinary arithmetic the solution would be to undo the forward 'multiply by 5' by doing the opposite, which is 'divide by 5'. However, the fact that numbers also get reduced modulo 26 in the forward process proves something of an obstacle to this plan. For example, dividing the C-number 22 by 5 produces 4·4, which is not in the set of P-numbers. Decimal numbers don't normally appear in cryptographic calculations, nor do the simplest of fractions, such as $\frac{1}{3}$. It's just the natural numbers most of the time, with the occasional negative whole number allowed for convenience.

So how to undo the forward action of 'multiply by 5 modulo 26'? I'm going to tell you how it is done, and the method will appear very mysterious. I'm only going to hint at an explanation of why it works. It is not that it is hard to explain, but to do so properly would involve too long a diversion from my main theme.

To convert the C-numbers back to their original P-counterparts, multiply them by 21 modulo 26.

"Did you say multiply? Surely there must be a division involved somewhere, and where does this magical number 21 come from?"

"Yes, I did say multiply and yes, you are right – there is a division involved somewhere."

"There doesn't appear to be."

"Agreed, but believe me that multiplying by 21 modulo 26 is equivalent in this arithmetic to multiplying by the fraction $\frac{1}{5}$ in ordinary arithmetic."

"I see. Well, I don't see, but I do understand that multiplying by $\frac{1}{5}$ in normal arithmetic is the same as dividing by 5."

"Yes, in everyday arithmetic the number $\frac{1}{5}$ is called the *multiplicative inverse* of 5."

"I remember. The number $\frac{1}{5}$ is the multiplicative inverse of 5 because when 5 is multiplied by $\frac{1}{5}$ the number 1 is obtained."

"Exactly. Now in arithmetic modulo 26, the number 21 is the multiplicative inverse of 5, because when 5 is multiplied by 21 and the result reduced modulo 26 the number 1 appears."

"That's kind of fun because you can't get the inverse by just 'turning the number upside down', as in ordinary arithmetic. Let me verify what you say. In ordinary arithmetic, $5 \times 21 = 105$, and since $105 = 4 \times 26 + 1$, it follows that $(5 \times 21) \bmod 26 = 1$."

"Impressed?"

"Yes, but I'd be more so if you could explain how you knew that 21 is the multiplicative inverse of 5 modulo 26, rather than producing it like a magician's white rabbit."

"I'm not going to tell you all my secrets, but you are right when you say that 21 is *the* multiplicative inverse of 5 modulo 26, because 21 is the only natural number between 0 and 25 that has this property."

"Thank you, I didn't realise I was being profound. I'm afraid I automatically assumed that the number 5 would have only one inverse."

"If you allow natural numbers greater than the modulus 26 and/or negative whole numbers, then it has an infinite number of 'inverses', two of which are -5 and 47, but this is beside the point."

"If you say so. I'm going to check that your deciphering rule really works. I'll try it on the C-number 22."

The calculation

$$
\begin{aligned}
22 \times 21 &= 462 \\
&= 17 \times 26 + 20 \\
\Rightarrow (22 \times 21) \bmod 26 &= 20
\end{aligned}
$$

verifies that the C-number 22 corresponds to the P-number 20, as it

In Code

should. Great!

The deciphering rule giving the P-number corresponding to a C-number (enciphered by $C = 5P \bmod 26$) is

$$P = 21C \bmod 26$$

Hence $K_D = 21$ is the deciphering key.

Summary: This particular cryptosystem enciphers via
$$C = 5P \bmod 26$$
and deciphers via
$$P = 21C \bmod 26$$
Its keys are
$$K_E = 5 \qquad K_D = 21$$

These keys are called single *parameter keys* because each is specified by a single number.

Let us see what happens when we try enciphering using the formula

$$C = 4P \bmod 26$$

The following array shows the results of enciphering the numbers 0 to 25 according to this rule:

P	$\to$	C		P	$\to$	C
0	$\to$	0		13	$\to$	0
1	$\to$	4		14	$\to$	4
2	$\to$	8		15	$\to$	8
3	$\to$	12		16	$\to$	12
4	$\to$	16		17	$\to$	16
5	$\to$	20		18	$\to$	20
6	$\to$	24		19	$\to$	24
7	$\to$	2		20	$\to$	2
8	$\to$	6		21	$\to$	6
9	$\to$	10		22	$\to$	10

10	→	14		23	→	14
11	→	18		24	→	18
12	→	22		25	→	22

Notice anything about the two C-number columns? They are identical. For example, the P-number 9 becomes the C-number 10 because

$$4 \times 9 = 36 = 1 \times 26 + 10 \Rightarrow (4 \times 9) \bmod 26 = 10$$

while the P-number 22 *also* becomes the C-number 10, because

$$4 \times 22 = 88 = 3 \times 26 + 10 \Rightarrow (4 \times 22) \bmod 26 = 10$$

This is not good. The table shows that the ordered set

$$\{0, 1, 2, 3, 4, 5, 6, 7, 8, 9, 10, 11, 12, 13, 14, 15, 16, 17, 18, 19, 20, 21, 22, 23, 24, 25\}$$

gets transformed by this enciphering rule into the ordered set

$$\{0, 4, 8, 12, 16, 20, 24, 2, 6, 10, 14, 18, 22\}$$

twice over. The set of C-numbers is not the original set of P-numbers rearranged in some order, but just one 'half' of that set. This time the correspondence between the set of P-numbers and the set of C-numbers is not a one-to-one correspondence but a 'two-to-one' correspondence, since two P-numbers correspond to every C-number. As verified, the numbers 9 and 22 both correspond to 10, which in terms of characters, means that the letters j and w both encipher as **k**. Such an enciphering rule is a disaster because the ciphertext character **k**, as is the case with each of the others, cannot be deciphered uniquely. Clearly this won't do.

Things are much worse when every P-number is multiplied by 13 modulo 26. Do a few multiplications and see.

In Code

I hope you are curious as to how 21 is found to be the (multiplicative) inverse of 5. One method is to multiply each of the numbers between 1 and 25 by 5 modulo 26 to see which produces an answer of 1. There is no point in your doing this for 5, now that you know the answer, so try 7 instead.

When you have found the inverse of 7 modulo 26, try to find the inverse of 4 modulo 26. (You need do no calculations as they are all done in the last array.) You'll get a surprise.

So now we have stumbled upon something very interesting by just experimenting. When we multiply P-numbers by 5 modulo 26 we get a one-to-one correspondence between the set of P-numbers and the set of C-numbers, and so obtain a valid cryptosystem, even if it is only a very simple one. On the other hand, when we multiply by 4 modulo 26 we fail to get the one-to-one correspondence that is so necessary to be able to encipher and decipher uniquely.

We can say that the enciphering rule

$$C = mP \bmod 26$$

works when $m = 5$ but not when $m = 4$, and we regard the number 5 as a 'good' m-value and the number 4 as a 'bad' m-value.

If we were to do some more playful experimenting, just trying different m values, then we'd find that the thirteen numbers 2, 4, 6, 8, 10, 12, 13, 14, 16, 18, 20, 22 and 24 are bad m-values, while the twelve numbers 1, 3, 5, 7, 9, 11, 15, 17, 19, 21, 23 and 25 are good m-values. For the modulus 26 there are only twelve good m-values. Granted, using the number 1 as a multiplier achieves no scrambling and so no enciphering, but it is still considered a good m-value because it gives a one-to-one correspondence between the set of P-numbers and the set of C-numbers (the identical correspondence).

So what property must a multiplier m have in order to guarantee a one-to-one correspondence between the set of P-numbers and the set of C-numbers? The answer is not so obvious but it is simple. The number m must have no factor other than 1 in common with the modulus 26.

If this condition is satisfied, things work; if not, they don't. It is a necessary and sufficient condition. Check this condition on the numbers above. All the numbers 2, 4, 6, 8, 10, 12, 13, 14, 16, 18, 20, 22 and 24 have either the factor 2 or 13 in common with 26, while the numbers 1, 3, 5, 7, 9, 11, 15, 17, 19, 21, 23 and 25 have no factor in common with 26 other than the trivial factor 1.

Two numbers are said to be *relatively prime* to each other whenever they have no non-trivial factor in common. (The answer in Appendix A to the Two jars puzzle gives another insight into this important concept.) Hence each of the numbers 1, 3, 5, 7, 9, 11, 15, 17, 19, 21, 23 and 25 is relatively prime to the number 26. In this terminology, the condition for a multiplier m to guarantee a one-to-one correspondence between the set of P-numbers and the set of C-numbers is that m be relatively prime to the modulus 26.

Thus there are only twelve choices for the multiplier m in the encipherment rule

$$C = mP \bmod 26$$

What about choosing a number m larger than 26? Try $m = 35$, and verify that it gives the same encipherment as $m = 9$. There is nothing new to be gained from using numbers bigger than the modulus. There really are only twelve good m-values. That said, how can we make things a tad more complicated while still working with the twenty-six characters of the lower-case alphabet?

Why not combine a multiplication with a shift? For example, follow multiplication by m with an addition (or shift) of s, so that the general encipherment rule is

$$C = (mP + s) \bmod 26$$

The enciphering key K_E associated with this enciphering rule is specified by two numbers: the multiplier m, which must be relatively prime to 26, and the shift s, which can be any number between 0 and 25.

Thus $K_E = \langle m, s \rangle$, read as 'the enciphering key m comma s', is a two-parameter key associated with the encipherment rule which

In Code

gives a one-to-one correspondence between plaintext and ciphertext. When $m = 1$, the encipherment rule reverts to a Caesar cipher with shift s. Since there are twelve choices for the first parameter m (the twelve 'good' m-values) and twenty-six for the second parameter s, there are $12 \times 26 = 312$ different keys in the keyspace.

When $K_E = \langle 5, 18 \rangle$ (read as 'the enciphering key 5 comma 18'), the encipherment rule is

$$C = (5P + 18) \bmod 26$$

It is straightforward to check that the set of P-numbers

$$\{0, 1, 2, 3, 4, 5, 6, 7, 8, 9, 10, 11, 12, 13, 14, 15, 16, 17, 18, 19, 20, 21, 22, 23, 24, 25\}$$

is transformed by this enciphering rule into the ordered set

$$\{18, 23, 2, 7, 12, 17, 22, 1, 6, 11, 16, 21, 0, 5, 10, 15, 20, 25, 4, 9, 14, 19, 24, 3, 8, 13\}$$

of C-numbers. Notice that the correspondence is one-to-one in nature.

Now for the interesting part. What is the deciphering key K_D corresponding to $K_E = \langle 5, 18 \rangle$? Answer:

$$K_D = \langle 21, 12 \rangle$$

(read as 'the deciphering key 21 comma 12'). Thus the deciphering rule is

$$P = (21C + 12) \bmod 26$$

I hear you protest, "Another white rabbit out of the magician's hat". Yes, but the rabbit number 21 you have seen before, undoing the forward action of multiplying by 5 modulo 26. For the moment I'm going to keep to myself how the number 12 gets in on the deciphering act. Here is how the deciphering works on the C-number 13:

$$P = (21 \times 13 + 12) \bmod 26 = 285 \bmod 26 = 25$$

since $285 = 10 \times 26 + 25$. If you check, you'll find that the P-number 25 does encipher as 13 under $C = (5P + 18) \bmod 26$.

S u m m a r y : For the system just described, the enciphering rule is

$$C = (5P + 18) \bmod 26$$

while the corresponding deciphering rule is

$$P = (21C + 12) \bmod 26$$

and the keys are $K_E = \langle 5, 18 \rangle$ and $K_D = \langle 21, 12 \rangle$.

Pairing Characters

Up to now we have been breaking plaintext into *single* characters, assigning each a numerical equivalent or P-number and enciphering that number, via some mathematical rule, to obtain a corresponding C-number. When this is done the plaintext can be regarded as having been enciphered (as numbers). If we wish, we can assign these C-numbers to their corresponding characters to obtain an encryption of the plaintext into 'true' ciphertext.

It should be clear that we can put much more distance between us and our enemy if we break plaintext into *blocks* of letters rather than into single characters. For example, working with the 26-character lower-case alphabet (for illustrative purposes only), we could break the plaintext

go placidly amid the noise and haste and

In Code

remember what peace there may be in silence

which contains sixty-nine characters (ignoring the blank spaces) into blocks of two:

go pl ac id ly am id th en oi se an dh as te an dr
em em be rw ha tp ea ce th er em ay be in si le nc ex

The x is appended to the last character e so that it too belongs to a complete block. In practice there is no need for this because a blank character is part of the underlying alphabet. Blocks consisting of two characters are known as *digraphs*.

How is each digraph enciphered into a unique 'ciphertext unit'? There are $26 \times 26 = 676$ possible digraphs, beginning with aa, ab, ac, ... , ba, bb, ... and ending with ... ya, yb, ... , zx, zy, zz. Why not assign each of them a unique number between 0 and 675 inclusive, and encrypt these numbers along lines similar to those for single characters?

A simple but effective scheme of assigning a unique number to each digraph is to assign the digraph aa the number 0, the digraph ab the number 1, and so on, with the digraph zz assigned the number 675. There is no need to look up a table to find the numerical equivalent (P-number) associated with a digraph: to determine the P-number for the digraph go, refer to the original table of numbers (associated with the 26 lower-case characters) to find the numerical equivalent of g as 6, and the numerical equivalent of o as 14. Then the P-number assigned to go is

$$P = (6 \times 26) + 14 = 170$$

Simple. Can you explain why this is correct?
The P-number assigned to og is

$$P = (14 \times 26) + 6 = 370$$

With this rule for assigning numerical equivalents, a program need

What Matters Is What's Left Over

only know the numbers associated with each of the single characters in the digraph, take note of their order, and compute the P-number as is done above.

The P-numbers of the set of digraphs given above are as follows:

170 401 002 211 310 012 211 501 117 372 472 013 085 018 498 013 095
116 116 030 464 182 509 104 056 501 121 116 024 030 221 476 290 340 127

There's safety in (BIG) numbers

So how might we encipher these P-numbers? Well, we could use a 'multiply and shift' encipherment rule like

$$C = (mP + s) \bmod n$$

as we did for single characters. But

1. What is the correct modulus n?
2. What multiplier m should be chosen?
3. What shift constant s can be used?

Answers:

1. The modulus n is 676, because the 676 distinct digraphs are assigned the whole numbers from 0 to 675.
2. The multiplier m may be any number between 1 and 675, provided it is relatively prime to 676. (There are 312 such numbers.)
3. The shift constant s may be any whole number in the range 0 to 675.

The keyspace for this cryptosystem has size $312 \times 676 = 210912$, which is considerably larger than the sizes of any of the previous keyspaces.

In Code

For example, choosing the key

$$K_E = \langle 159, 580 \rangle$$

makes the enciphering rule

$$C = (159P + 580) \bmod 676$$

Then the C-number corresponding to the P-number 170 (which is the numerical equivalent of the digraph go) is calculated as follows:

$$C = (159 \times 170 + 580) \bmod 676$$
$$= 27610 \bmod 676$$
$$\Rightarrow C = 570$$

since $27610 = 40 \times 676 + 570$.

How is 570 expressed as 'true' ciphertext? Because

$$570 = (21 \times 26) + 24$$

and 21 and 24 are the numerical equivalents of the letters **v** and **y**, respectively, the ciphertext unit corresponding to go is **vy**. Thus

$$\text{go} \rightarrow \text{vy}$$

Using the enciphement rule the C-numbers corresponding to the plaintext P-numbers are

570 119 222 329 522 460 329 471 255 240 592 619 575 062 670 619 137
096 096 618 672 450 391 216 020 471 215 096 340 618 567 552 046 560 493

This jumble of numbers can be converted into a string of ciphertext digraphs to give

**vo el ic md uy rm md sh jn ji we xn wh cs ze xn fr
dm dm xe zw ra pp ia ae sh ir dm ny xe vn vi be vc sx**

What Matters Is What's Left Over

Thus the encipherment of the plaintext

> go placidly amid the noise and haste and
> remember what peace there may be in silence

is

> **voelicmduyrmmdshjnjiwexnwhcszexnfr**
> **dmdmxezwrappiaaeshirdmnyxevnvibevcsx**

Here, without a word of explanation (but see Appendix C), is the deciphering rule:

$$P = (659C + 396) \bmod 676$$

This means that the deciphering key is $K_D = \langle 659,396 \rangle$. Let's decipher the C-number 493, which is the final one above, using this rule:

$$P = (659 \times 493 + 396) \bmod 676$$
$$= 325283 \bmod 676$$
$$\Rightarrow P = 127$$

since $325283 = 481 \times 676 + 127$.

Check that this is the correct P-value, either by consulting the set of P-numbers above or by re-enciphering it.

The simple device of partitioning plaintext into blocks consisting of two characters has greatly increased the size of the keyspace, even for a 26-letter alphabet. Using digraph encipherment with a 127-letter alphabet increases the size of the keyspace to over 258 million possibilities. This observation is not meant to suggest that this form of enciphering is secure. What it does show is that some avenues of attack, such as searching a keyspace, can be made computationally prohibitive for an enemy. (In fact, because much work has been done on the frequency analysis of digraphs, such encipherment is no longer used.)

In Code

Bigger Blocks

The enciphering of the 69 characters of

> go placidly amid the noise and haste and
> remember what peace there may be in silence

using blocks of three characters, or *trigraphs*, begins with the partition

> gop lac idl yam idt hen ois ean dha ste and
> rem emb erw hat pea cet her ema ybe ins ile nce

Since the total number of possible trigraphs is $26^3 = 17576$, each trigraph can be assigned a unique number from 0 to 17575. One way of doing this is illustrated for the trigraph gop. Since the numerical equivalents of the single characters g, o and p are 6, 14 and 15, respectively, the P-number assigned to the trigraph gop is

$$(6 \times 26^2) + (14 \times 26) + 15 = 4056 + 364 + 15 = 4435$$

These are the P-numbers for all the trigraphs:

> 4435 7438 5497 16236 5505 4849 9690 2717 2210 12666 341
> 11608 3017 3168 4751 10244 1475 4853 3016 16254 5764 5698 8844

If the same encipherment rule as already described for digraphs is used with the modulus 17576, then the ciphertext number corresponding to the P-number 4435 is

$$C = [(159 \times 4435) + 580] \bmod 17576 = 2705$$

Because

$$2705 = (4 \times 26^2) + (0 \times 26) + 1$$

92

and since the numbers 4, 0 and 1 are the numerical equivalents of the letters **e**, **a** and **b**, respectively, the encipherment gives

$$\text{gop} \rightarrow \textbf{eab}$$

The complete encipherment of

> go placidly amid the noise and haste and
> remember what peace there may be in silence

is

eabiiotupxrsvrnxjvsakpxvaripzudbr
bdsimlrzwainsiijunyihigibxuepkpbubau

This is a completely different encipherment to the one obtained using digraphs.

The plaintext may be partitioned into blocks of length 23:

> goplacidlyamidthenoisea ndhasteandrememberwhatp
> eacetheremaybeinsilence

The total number of blocks of length 23 is

$$n = 26^{23} = 350571449822005752615313090805756$$

which is a 'fairly big' number, though by comparison with the numbers used in modern cryptography it is a toddler. Assigning the three blocks a P-number in the range 0 to n using a similar procedure to those already described gives the P-numbers

> 88389774112496488148491229603504
> 176823017496378363396475650125589
> 53929205030218752977105934412508

There is a multitude of encipherment rules of the form

$$C = (mP + s) \bmod n$$

corresponding to the different choices of *m* and *s*, any of which may be chosen. One such has the enciphering key

$$K_E = \langle 16254753598124455839287703069565,$$
$$4934780421655195321883198047351 \rangle$$

because $m = 16254753598124455839287703069565$ has no factor, other than 1, in common with $n = 3205714498220057526153130$ 9080576. In this case the *P*-numbers become the *C*-numbers

$$3250332474585831270389763206181 99$$
$$1618356992460696894689938310924 84$$
$$2839863216990255560670365800534 75$$

The ciphertext blocks of length 23 corresponding to these numbers are

ydigsikvpswonjdqeasgszgh   maiyyygmlgalquxomyxxvua
vccniaasyjkvkwlugphrimt

This time,

go placidly amid the noise and haste and
remember what peace there may be in silence

enciphers as

ydigsikvpswonjdqeasgszghmaiyyygmlg
alquxomyxxvuavccniaasyjkvkwlugphrimt

This last example helps us to appreciate how big the numbers can get when plaintext is partitoned into even moderately sized blocks. Although cryptosystems based on enciphering blocks of plaintext by the 'multiply and shift' rules I have described are vulnerable to various forms of attack, modern systems rely in part for their security on the 'blocking' of plaintext into huge blocks.

What Matters Is What's Left Over

When the modulus is a 200-digit number the blocks of text can be of length 95 or more, and the number of different blocks of this length is astronomical.

It is unsatisfactory to have exhibited deciphering rules without explanation. If in so doing I have made them appear mysterious but aroused your curiosity, then this is something positive. However, it may be that you are totally frustrated by not knowing how they are obtained. It is easy to determine the deciphering rule corresponding to an enciphering rule of the type described if one knows how to obtain the multiplicative inverse of a number (with respect to a modulus). Appendix C gives a short account of a wonderfully efficient procedure known to Euclid for calculating the greatest common divisor of two natural numbers. This allows the inverse of a number to be calculated, and leads to an explanation of how those deciphering rules are obtained.

I'm sure that other questions will have occured to you. One is "How many natural numbers less than a given number are relatively prime to it?" As we shall see, this is a particularly important question in cryptography.

Functions: Notion and Notation

Each of the enciphering rules:

$$C = (P + 3) \bmod 26$$
$$C = 5P \bmod 26$$
$$C = 4P \bmod 26$$
$$C = (5P + 18) \bmod 26$$
$$C = (159P + 580) \bmod 676$$

transforms a set of P-numbers into a set of C-numbers. Whether or not, from the viewpoint of cryptography, these rules are chosen cleverly, their function is to convert P-numbers into C-numbers. Each is a *function* which describes the desired mathematical action

In Code

to be performed on a typical *P*-number in order to generate the corresponding *C*-number.

Since the first letter of the word 'function' is *f*, this letter is often used to stand for the function to be performed on a *P*-number to produce a *C*-number:

$$C = f(P)$$

read as '*f* of *P*'. (The notation does *not* mean *f* multiplied by *P*, which would be written simply as *fP*, if *f* and *P* both stood for numbers.)

Although the symbol *P* in *f*(*P*) stands for a number, the symbol *f* stands for the operation which is to be performed on the number *P* (to produce the number *C*). Until the function *f* is explicitly specified by some mathematical formula, we don't know the exact rule by which the *C*-numbers are calculated. We only know in abstract terms that the *C*-numbers are 'a function of' the *P*-numbers. The manner in which they are computed depends on a non-specified action *f* applied to the *P*-numbers. When the function is expressed by a formula, such as

$$f(P) = P^3$$

then the action of *f* on *P* is specified. In this case the function *f* takes each *P* and computes its 'cube', P^3, to obtain the corresponding *C*-value. Thus if *P* is replaced by 2 in the formula, then

$$f(2) = 2^3 = 8$$

The effect of applying the function *f* to the *P*-number 2 is to cube it, to get the *C*-number 8. Also, because

$$f(5) = 5^3 = 125$$

the function *f* 'maps' the *P*-number 5 into the *C*-number 125. Expressed generally in words, the function *f* takes a number and cubes it. This particular function f could be named the 'cubing function'.

The five enciphering rules listed on page 95 are thus the functions

$$f(P) = (P + 3)\bmod 26$$
$$f(P) = 5P\bmod 26$$
$$f(P) = 4P\bmod 26$$
$$f(P) = (5P + 18)\bmod 26$$
$$f(P) = (159P + 580)\bmod 676$$

respectively. When the function f is the third of these, then $C = f(P)$ translates to

$$C = 4P\bmod 26$$

and for the fourth function f, $C = f(P)$ translates to

$$C = (5P + 18)\bmod 26$$

There is a world of a difference between using the first and the second of these two functions as an enciphering rule in a cryptosystem. You may recall that the first one does not map the twenty-six P-numbers $\{0, 1, 2, ..., 24, 25\}$ onto a set consisting of twenty-six different C-numbers. Instead it maps these twenty-six P-numbers onto the set $\{0, 2, ..., 22, 24\}$ consisting of just thirteeen different numbers. Here each C-number has two different P-numbers associated with it. Consequently, it is worthless as an enciphering function because it does not allow a C-number to be deciphered uniquely – it does not establish a one-to-one corres-pondence between the set of P-numbers and the set of C-numbers. In mathematical terms, it is not a *one-to-one function*.

It should be obvious that enciphering functions *must* be one-to-one to ensure unique decipherment. The function $f(P) = (5P + 18)\bmod 26$ is a one-to-one function and so can be used as an enciphering function. It establishes a one-to-one correspondence between the set of twenty-six P-numbers $\{0, 1, 2, ..., 23, 24, 25\}$ and a set of *C*-numbers, which also consists of twenty-six numbers; in fact it is the original set of numbers ordered in a different way. Under the transformation induced by this function *f*, each *P*-number is assigned a unique *C*-number and, crucially, each *C*-number is associated with one and only one *P*-number. With the exception of $f(P) = 4P \bmod 26$, all the other functions listed above are also one-to-one functions and so can be used as enciphering transformations.

In general, the function that undoes the action of a one-to-one function *f* is called its *inverse function*. It is written as f^{-1} (for reasons we need not go into) and is read as '*f* inverse'. In cryptography the deciphering function is the one that undoes the (forward) action of the enciphering function. If the (one-to-one) enciphering function is denoted by *f*, then the corresponding deciphering function is denoted by f^{-1} . Because f^{-1} reverses or 'inverts' the action of *f* by mapping *C*-numbers (back) to *P*-numbers, we can write

$$P = f^{-1}(C)$$

This notation shows f^{-1} acting on *C* to produce *P*.

In most cases, the formula or rule specifying the deciphering function is different from the rule describing the enciphering function. For example, if the enciphering function is

$$f(P) = (5P + 18) \bmod 26$$

then the deciphering function is

$$f^{-1}(C) = (21C + 12) \bmod 26$$

For the sake of emphasis, let's check that f^{-1} undoes the action of *f* on the specific number 19. Applying the enciphering function *f* first gives

$$f(19) = [(5 \times 19) + 18] \bmod 26 = 113 \bmod 26 = 9$$

because $113 = 4 \times 26 + 9$. Applying the deciphering function f^{-1} to this result then gives

$$f^{-1}(9) = [(21 \times 9) + 12] \bmod 26 = 201 \bmod 26 = 19$$

because $201 = 7 \times 26 + 19$. Thus

$$f^{-1}(9) = 19$$

verifying that f^{-1} undoes the action of f on $P = 19$.

Since $f(19) = 9$, replacing the 9 in the equation $f^{-1}(9) = 19$ makes it

$$f^{-1}(f(19)) = 19$$

It is usual to replace the 'outer' pair of round brackets ( ) by a pair of square brackets [ ] thus:

$$f^{-1}[f(19)] = 19$$

This can be interpreted as saying that performing the function f on 19, and following this by performing the function f^{-1} on the result, gets us back to 19.

In general, since f^{-1} undoes what f does, then following the action of f on P by that of f^{-1} on the result has the effect of reproducing P, a fact which is expressed concisely by writing

$$f^{-1}[f(P)] = P$$

In terms of enciphering and deciphering, this simply says that decrypting what has been encrypted returns the original plaintext.

A Cryptosystem

The function notation allows us to describe in simple terms the

In Code

general character of a cryptosystem. Such a system essentially consists of an enciphering function or transformation f, which does the encrypting, and a deciphering transformation f^{-1} which does the decrypting. The equation

$$C = f(P)$$

represents f acting on a typical plaintext number P to give its corresponding ciphertext number C, while the equation

$$P = f^{-1}(C)$$

represents f^{-1} acting on a typical ciphertext number C to restore the original plaintext number P.

Usually a cryptosystem is thought of not as one enciphering function along with its associated deciphering function, but as a family of enciphering functions and corresponding deciphering functions. For example, for a fixed modulus n, each member f of the family of 'multiply and shift' enciphering transformations has the form

$$C = f(P) = (mP + s) \bmod n$$

for a particular pair of values of the parameters m and s. The number of different enciphering functions is determined by the number of distinct pairs $\langle m, s \rangle$. If this 'cryptosystem' were to be used as a general system by a number of people, then each of the users would have their own special enciphering key, $K_E = \langle m, s \rangle$. This key has a unique deciphering key, K_D, associated with it which determines the corresponding deciphering transformation f^{-1}.

According to Kerckhoff's principle, the users of such a system should assume that the general method by which they encipher messages is public knowledge. Their confidence in whether or not the system is any good should depend only on believing that keeping the keys secret ensures secure communication. Apparently, in this case, it would be a mistaken belief even for a very large modulus.

What Matters Is What's Left Over

Because the letters P and C are the initials of the words plaintext and ciphertext, respectively, it is natural for the enciphering and deciphering functions to be described by the equations

$$C = f(P) \quad P = f^{-1}(C)$$

However, when the letters P and C are replaced by the more commonly used x and y, the equations read

$$y = f(x) \quad x = f^{-1}(y)$$

This familiar notation will be used later when discussing the remote coin tossing protocol used by two of cryptography's best known personages – Alice and Bob.

4 . Sums with a Difference

*I*n this chapter you get a chance to learn the powerful arithmetic used in cryptography. This arithmetic can give answers to problems in just two or three steps where ordinary arithmetic would require massive amounts of calculation. Along the way we'll learn about the rule of nines, how books are assigned ISBN numbers, googols, a mistaken belief of the ancient Chinese, pseudoprimes, Carmichael numbers and the Little Theorem of Fermat. We'll discover the almost incredible fact that a number can be declared to be composite without a single factor having been found. We also talk a little about the problem of *primality* which is that of finding primes, and make clear the separate nature of its sister problem, *factorisation*.

More on Days of the Week

Let's return to the problem in which we assume that today is Sunday and are interested in knowing what day of the week it will be one hundred days from now. Suppose we assign the number 0 to this Sunday. Then to tomorrow, Monday, we assign the number 1, with Tuesday being assigned 2, and so on to next Saturday, which is assigned the number 6. Thus we have the following correspondences between the numbers 0, 1, 2, 3, 4, 5, 6 and the days of this week, which starts today, Sunday:

Sums with a Difference

$$
\begin{array}{rcl}
\text{Sunday} & \longleftrightarrow & 0 \\
\text{Monday} & \longleftrightarrow & 1 \\
\text{Tuesday} & \longleftrightarrow & 2 \\
\text{Wednesday} & \longleftrightarrow & 3 \\
\text{Thursday} & \longleftrightarrow & 4 \\
\text{Friday} & \longleftrightarrow & 5 \\
\text{Saturday} & \longleftrightarrow & 6 \\
\end{array}
$$

It is then natural that all future Sundays be assigned the numbers 7, 14, 21, ... in succession. We can even assign numbers to all past Sundays by labelling last Sunday with the negative number -7, the Sunday before that with the number -14, and so on for all the Sundays receding into the far-off past. Thus the infinite set of integers (whole numbers)

$$\{\ldots, -21, -14, -7, \mathbf{0}, 7, 14, 21, \ldots\}$$

contains the numerical labels of all Sundays, past, present and future. We could call this set 'the set of Sundays'. By the same token, the following infinite sets of integers contain the numerical labels of all past and future

$$
\begin{array}{rl}
\text{Mondays:} & \{\ldots, -20, -13, -6, \mathbf{1}, 8, 15, 22, \ldots\} \\
\text{Tuesdays:} & \{\ldots, -19, -12, -5, \mathbf{2}, 9, 16, 23, \ldots\} \\
\text{Wednesdays:} & \{\ldots, -18, -11, -4, \mathbf{3}, 10, 17, 24, \ldots\} \\
\text{Thursdays:} & \{\ldots, -17, -10, -3, \mathbf{4}, 11, 18, 25, \ldots\} \\
\text{Fridays:} & \{\ldots, -16, -9, -2, \mathbf{5}, 12, 19, 26, \ldots\} \\
\text{Saturdays:} & \{\ldots, -15, -8, -1, \mathbf{6}, 13, 20, 27, \ldots\} \\
\end{array}
$$

These sets have no element in common (how could the set of Mondays, say, have an element in common with the set of Fridays?) but between them they give the full set of integers

$$\{\ldots, -4, -3, -2, -1, \mathbf{0}, 1, 2, 3, 4, \ldots\}$$

This is hardly a surprise since the number 0 is associated with today,

103

In Code

the positive integers with all future days and the negative integers with all the days that have passed. So every integer lies in one of these sets, and in one set only.

All the numbers in the Tuesdays-set

$$\{ \dots, -19, -12, -5, \mathbf{2}, 9, 16, 23, \dots \}$$

leave the remainder 2 when divided by 7, even the negative ones. For example, since -19 can be written as $-3 \times 7 + 2$, we say that the remainder when -19 is divided by 7 is 2. Although -19 is also equal to $-2 \times 7 + (-5)$, the number -5 is not regarded as the remainder of -19 upon division by 7. The convention with respect to a remainder is that it must be either 0 or a positive integer less than the modulus. For division by 7 this means that it is one (and only one) of 0, 1, 2, 3, 4, 5, 6. The fact that every integer in the Tuesdays-set leaves a remainder of 2 when divided by 7 may strike you as nothing more than obvious. The technical term for this set is 'the residue class 2 modulo 7'. The word *residue* is just another word for remainder, and *class* is just another word for set.

Similarly, every integer in the Wednesdays-set leaves a remainder of 3 when divided by 7; this is the residue class 3 modulo 7. Similar results and names apply to the other sets. So if you need to know to which residue class a given integer belongs, all you have to do is find the remainder obtained when the number is divided by the modulus 7, or, as we say more briefly, 'its remainder modulo 7'. The calculation

$$100 = 14 \times 7 + 2 \Rightarrow 100 \bmod 7 = 2$$

tells us that the number 100 lies in the residue class 2 modulo 7.

Two integers, call them a and b, belong to the same residue class modulo 7 if and only if

$$a \bmod 7 = b \bmod 7$$

This is one way of saying that they both leave the same remainder

Sums with a Difference

upon division by 7. Thus, to find whether 675 and 943 lie in the same residue class modulo 7, calculate $675 \bmod 7$ and $943 \bmod 7$ to see whether these two numbers match. Of course, in the context of weekdays, lying in the same class means that both integers represent the same day of the week. Since $675 \bmod 7 = 3$ and $943 \bmod 7 = 5$, we see that 675 days from now it will be a Wednesday, while 943 days from now it will be a Friday. Thus 675 and 943 lie in different residue classes modulo 7.

Whereas finding their respective remainders allows us to determine the days of the week associated with two numbers, there is a much faster way of deciding whether two integers belong to the same residue class. It is clear that the integers in any particular class differ from one another by a multiple of 7 since, for example, all Tuesdays are 'full weeks' apart. This means that for any two integers a and b to be in the same residue class, their difference, $a - b$, should be exactly divisible by 7.

Some Notation

We write $m \mid n$ (and say 'm divides n') when the integer m divides exactly into the integer n and write $m \nmid n$ (and say 'm does not divide n') when it doesn't. So, for example, $7 \mid 21$ but $7 \nmid 22$. Similarly, $11 \mid 132$ while $15 \nmid 26$.

So, if two integers a and b are such that $7 \mid (a - b)$ (meaning that their difference $a - b$ is exactly divisible by 7), then they lie in the same residue class modulo 7. It is customary to write $7 \mid a - b$ rather than $7 \mid (a - b)$. If $7 \nmid a - b$, then their difference is not divisible by 7, and a and b lie in different residue classes. For example, to show that the numbers 855 and 127 lie in the same residue class, we calculate their difference $855 - 127$ to be 728 and then check whether $7 \mid 728$. It does, because $728 = 104 \times 7$.

In terms of days of the week, the numbers 127 and 855 represent the same weekday. Note that though the above calculation tells us that these two weekdays lie a full 104 weeks apart, it does not indicate which day of the week they both represent. This extra

In Code

information is obtained by working out that $127 \bmod 7 = 1$ or $855 \bmod 7 = 1$. This shows that each of them represents a Monday.

On the other hand, the numbers 943 and 675 lie in different sets because their difference, $943 - 675 = 268$, is not divisible by 7, as the calculation $268 = 38 \times 7 + 2$ shows. This calculation gives no indication of the different days represented by 943 and 675, but it does reveal that they represent weekdays which are two days apart. If the number 675 represents a Wednesday, which day of the week does the number 943 represent?

A New Arithmetic

Carl Friedrich Gauss, the young German mathematician I mentioned earlier (a portrait of whom in later life now adorns the 10-Deutschmark note), introduced the notation

$$a \equiv b \,(\bmod m)$$

to indicate that the integers a and b lie in the same residue class modulo m. (Read $a \equiv b \,(\bmod m)$ as 'a is congruent to b, modulo m'.)

The letter m, standing for the modulus, is always a natural number. So far we have been working with the modulus $m = 7$. For example, $38 \equiv 17 \,(\bmod 7)$ because 38 and 17 both lie in the residue class 3 modulo 7. Thus we say that 38 is congruent to 17 modulo 7. We also say that 38 and 17 are congruent modulo 7.

The notation $a \not\equiv b \,(\bmod m)$ can be read as 'a is not congruent to b, modulo m'. It means that a and b do not lie in the same residue class modulo m. In this case a and b are said to be incongruent modulo m, so $a \not\equiv b \,(\bmod m)$ is also read as 'a and b are incongruent modulo m.' For example, $24 \not\equiv 16 \,(\bmod 5)$ because 24 lies in the residue class 4 modulo 5, while 16 lies in the residue class 1 modulo 5. Thus 24 and 16 are incongruent modulo 5.

You may have noticed that the symbol 'mod' is now being used in a different role, and appears between brackets followed by the modulus m. In our earlier use it appears without brackets, followed

106

Sums with a Difference

by the modulus m. However, there is a connection between the two uses.

Whereas the expression $100 \bmod 7$ is the remainder when 100 is divided by 7, the expression $100 \equiv 86 \pmod 7$ says that 100 and 86 lie in the same residue class modulo 7. But these numbers lie in the same residue class modulo 7 if and only if they leave the same remainder when divided by 7, i.e. if and only if

$$100 \bmod 7 = 86 \bmod 7$$

They are, since both are 2. In general,

$$a \equiv b \pmod m \text{ if and only if } a \bmod m = b \bmod m$$

This relation displays the two different uses of the mod symbol. It also tells us that if we want to check whether $a \equiv b \pmod m$, then all we need do is check whether $a \bmod m = b \bmod m$.

But you may recall from our discussion of residue classes modulo 7 that there is a far easier way. To check whether $a \equiv b \pmod m$, all you need do is check whether their difference, $a - b$, is divisible by m, since then and only then do a and b lie in the same residue class modulo m. Thus

$$a \equiv b \pmod m \quad \text{if and only if} \quad m \mid a - b$$

This criterion is the simplest way of checking whether $a \equiv b \pmod m$.

We can confirm that $38 \equiv 17 \pmod 7$ by showing that the difference $38 - 17 = 21$ is divisible by 7. But $7 \mid 21$ because $21 = 3 \times 7$. Normally we are not as longwinded as this. To check whether $38 \equiv 17 \pmod 7$ we simply write $7 \mid 38 - 17 = 21$. The expression $38 - 17 = 21$ to the right of the divisibility symbol $\mid$ is the difference between 38 and 17, being calculated as 21. Then the expression is interpreted as reading $7 \mid 21$. On the other hand, $24 \not\equiv 16 \pmod 7$ because $24 - 16 = 8$ is not divisible by 7. As above, we might simply write $24 \not\equiv 16 \pmod 7$ because $7 \nmid 24 - 16 = 8$.

In Code

Gauss deliberately used the symbol $\equiv$ because of its resemblance to the equality symbol $=$. He developed a new arithmetic similar to ordinary arithmetic which is ideally suited for calculating with remainders.

Now for a short tour of some of the features of this arithmetic. (A note on terminology: $32 \equiv 14 \pmod 9$ is often termed a 'congruence with respect to the modulus 9', or a 'congruence modulo 9' or simply a 'congruence' when the modulus is understood.)

Arithmetic Properties of Congruences

Multiplication by a Constant

A congruence can be multiplied on both sides by the same whole number to get another valid congruence.

Multiplying both sides of the congruence $32 \equiv 14 \pmod 9$ by 8 gives
$$32 \times 8 \equiv 14 \times 8 \pmod 9$$

Performing ordinary multiplication on both sides of the congruence gives
$$256 \equiv 112 \pmod 9$$

Check: Since $9 \mid 256 - 112 = 144$, this congruence is true.

Exponentiation

Both sides of a congruence can be raised to the same positive number (often called the *power* or *exponent*). This is called *exponentiating* the congruence.

For example, raising each side of the congruence
$$32 \equiv 14 \pmod 9$$

108

Sums with a Difference

to the power 3 gives

$$32^3 \equiv 14^3 \pmod 9$$

This says that

$$32768 \equiv 2744 \pmod 9$$

C h e c k : Since $32768 - 2744 = 30024 = 3336 \times 9$, this is a valid congruence.

Addition, Subtraction and Multiplication

Two congruences *with respect to the same modulus* can be 'added', 'subtracted' and 'multiplied'. This is illustrated by the two congruences

$$32 \equiv 14 \pmod 9 \qquad 25 \equiv 7 \pmod 9$$

These congruences are 'added' as follows:

$$
\begin{array}{r}
32 \equiv 14 \pmod 9 \\
25 \equiv 7 \pmod 9 \\
\hline
57 \equiv 21 \pmod 9
\end{array}
$$

C h e c k : Here, ordinary addition is carried out on the left- and right-hand sides to give the single congruence

$$57 \equiv 21 \pmod 9$$

Is this a true statement? Yes, because $9 \mid 57 - 21 = 36$. Great!

The same two congruences are 'subtracted' as follows:

$$
\begin{array}{r}
32 \equiv 14 \pmod 9 \\
25 \equiv 7 \pmod 9 \\
\hline
7 \equiv 7 \pmod 9
\end{array}
$$

C h e c k : Here, ordinary subtraction is carried out on the left- and right-hand sides to give the single congruence:

$$7 \equiv 7 \,(\mathrm{mod}\,9)$$

This is also true because $9\,|\,7 - 7 = 0$.

The same two congruences are 'multiplied' as follows:

$$
\begin{array}{r}
32 \equiv 14 \,(\mathrm{mod}\,9) \\
25 \equiv 7 \,(\mathrm{mod}\,9) \\
\hline
800 \equiv 98 \,(\mathrm{mod}\,9)
\end{array}
$$

Here, ordinary multiplication is carried out on the left- and right-hand sides to give the single congruence

$$800 \equiv 98 \,(\mathrm{mod}\,9)$$

Check: Since $800 - 98 = 702 = 78 \times 9$, this congruence is also valid.

Remark: We don't talk (at this stage at any rate) about 'dividing' congruences since we are dealing only with whole numbers and not fractions.

The properties illustrated for the modulus 9 are also valid for any other natural number modulus. You might like to make up your own examples using a different modulus.

The transitive property

In ordinary arithmetic this property says that if $a = b$ and $b = c$, then $a = c$, something which may strike you as obvious. This property is also valid in our new arithmetic. For example,

if $147 \equiv 84 \,(\mathrm{mod}\,9)$ and $84 \equiv 3 \,(\mathrm{mod}\,9)$ then $147 \equiv 3 \,(\mathrm{mod}\,9)$

Check that all these congruences are true.

Sums with a Difference

The first congruence says that 147 and 84 are in the same residue class modulo 9, while the second says that 84 and 3 are in the same residue class modulo 9. Hence it is obvious that 147 and 3 are also in the same residue class modulo 9, or equivalently that $147 \equiv 3 \pmod 9$.

In a Million Days' Time

To determine which day of the week it will be a million days from now, begin with

$$10 \equiv 3 \pmod 7$$

Now square both sides of this congruence to get

$$100 \equiv 9 \pmod 7$$

Since $9 \equiv 2 \pmod 7$, the transitive property says that

$$100 \equiv 2 \pmod 7$$

Since 100 cubed is 1000000, cube both sides of this congruence to get

$$1000000 \equiv 8 \pmod 7$$

Since $8 \equiv 1 \pmod 7$, the transitive property gives

$$1000000 \equiv 1 \pmod 7$$

Thus the number 1000000 is in the residue class 1 modulo 7. In the context of days of the week, if today is Sunday then in one million days' time it will be a Monday. We have arrived at this result almost effortlessly, by using some properties of congruences along with a few simple multiplications and divisions.

However, you might say, "Wouldn't it be easier (if less elegant) to find $10^6 \bmod 7$ simply by using short division to get

$$7)\overline{\underset{142857 + 1}{1000000}}$$

This calculation tells me that a million days consist of 142857 weeks with a day to spare." It may appear to be just as easy to tackle the problem this way, because dividing by 7 isn't that hard, even though it does involve six divisions and six 'carries'. But I'll say to you, "OK, smarty, which day of the week will it be in 10^{100} days time?"

Googol

The number 10^{100} has one hundred and one digits, beginning with 1 and followed by a hundred 0's. It is known as a 'googol', a name invented by a nine-year-old American boy. Numbers of this magnitude are commonplace in cryptography.

Knowing the congruence $1000000 \equiv 1 \,(\bmod\, 7)$ allows us to show that the googol, 10^{100}, leaves a remainder of 4 when divided by 7. This is done *without* knowing how often 7 divides into this gigantic number. Here's how.

Since $1000000 = 10^6$, we know from the 'million days' time' calculation that

$$10^6 \equiv 1 \,(\bmod\, 7)$$

The 1 on the right-hand side of this congruence is very convenient. Why? Because no matter to what power 1 is raised it still remains a 1. Watch how this property is exploited. We raise both sides of the congruence to the power of 16 because $(10^6)^{16} = 10^{96}$ (note that $(10^6)^{17} = 10^{102}$ makes the power exceed 100). We get

$$10^{96} \equiv 1 \,(\bmod\, 7)$$

We're nearly there. To finish, we need to multiply 10^{96} by 10^4 to get 10^{100}. Since $10^2 \equiv 2 \,(\bmod\, 7) \Rightarrow 10^4 \equiv 4 \,(\bmod\, 7)$, the multiplication

Sums with a Difference

$$10^{96} \equiv 1 \pmod 7$$
$$\underline{10^4 \equiv 4 \pmod 7}$$
$$10^{100} \equiv 4 \pmod 7$$

shows that

$$10^{100} \equiv 4 \pmod 7$$

So if today is a Sunday, then in 10^{100} days' time it will be Thursday. You shouldn't go through life without knowing this!

A Special Property of the Number 9

We'll put the new arithmetic to work to show you a property of the number 9. So for the next few pages we'll be working with the modulus 9.

Beginning with the fact that

$$10 \equiv 1 \pmod 9$$

and squaring both sides of the congruence, that is, raising each side to the power 2, gives

$$10^2 \equiv 1 \pmod 9$$

Is this true? To show that $10^2 \equiv 1 \pmod 9$ we must verify that $9 \mid 10^2 - 1$. Since $10^2 - 1 = 100 - 1 = 99$, this is clearly the case.

Cubing both sides of the original congruence gives

$$10^3 \equiv 1 \pmod 9$$

This is also true since $10^3 - 1 = 1000 - 1 = 999$ is divisible by 9. Similarly,

$$10^4 \equiv 1 \pmod 9$$

Check: $10^4 - 1 = 10000 - 1 = 9999$ is divisible by 9. By now

113

you will have guessed that it doesn't matter to what power 10 is raised, the result is always congruent to 1 modulo 9. That is,

$$10^n \equiv 1 \, (\mathrm{mod} \, 9)$$

for each natural number n. It is also true for $n = 0$ because $10^0 = 1$. Put another way, this says that $1 \equiv 1 \, (\mathrm{mod} \, 9)$.

If, for the following four congruences modulo 9,

$$1000 \equiv 1 \, (\mathrm{mod} \, 9)$$
$$100 \equiv 1 \, (\mathrm{mod} \, 9)$$
$$10 \equiv 1 \, (\mathrm{mod} \, 9)$$
$$1 \equiv 1 \, (\mathrm{mod} \, 9)$$

we multiply the first by 3, the second by 5, the third by 4 and the fourth by 8, then we get

$$3000 \equiv 3 \, (\mathrm{mod} \, 9)$$
$$500 \equiv 5 \, (\mathrm{mod} \, 9)$$
$$40 \equiv 4 \, (\mathrm{mod} \, 9)$$
$$8 \equiv 8 \, (\mathrm{mod} \, 9)$$

Since these congruences are all modulo 9 they can be added (on each side) to give

$$3548 \equiv 3 + 5 + 4 + 8 \, (\mathrm{mod} \, 9)$$

We have deliberately refrained from actually adding $3 + 5 + 4 + 8$ to get 20. Now that we have done so, we can verify that the congruence is true because $3458 - 20 = 3438 = 382 \times 9$.

So where is all this going? We have discovered that the number 3458 is congruent to 'the sum of its digits' modulo 9. This is true of every natural number n. In general, if s is the sum of the digits representing n, then

$$n \equiv s \, (\mathrm{mod} \, 9)$$

114

Sums with a Difference

This means that n and s *always* lie in the same residue class modulo 9, or equivalently that $9 \mid n - s$.

If $n = 83725163$, then $s = 8 + 3 + 7 + 2 + 5 + 1 + 6 + 3 = 35$ and

$$n - s = 83725163 - 35 = 83725128 = 9302792 \times 9$$

shows that $9 \mid n - s$, or equivalently that $n \equiv s \pmod 9$.

Now for a small piece of cleverness which will tell us in which residue class modulo 9 both n and s lie. Applying the same result to $s = 35$ gives

$$35 \equiv 3 + 5 = 8 \pmod 9$$

Thus $s \bmod 9 = 8$, and so $n \bmod 9 = 8$ also. Hence 83725163 and 35 both lie in the residue class 8 modulo 9. It is easy to verify this result for 35 because $35 = 3 \times 9 + 8$.

The Rule of Nines

This rule says that an integer is divisible by 9 if and only if the sum of its digits is divisible by 9.

Here is the explanation. If the sum s of the digits of a number is divisible by 9, then $s \equiv 0 \pmod 9$. Since $n \equiv s \pmod 9$ in general, in this particular case $n \equiv 0 \pmod 9$ also. But $n \equiv 0 \pmod 9$ means that the number n itself is divisible by 9.

Knowing this rule might get you looking at car registration numbers to see whether or not they are divisible by 9. When summing the digits you can save work by continually reducing modulo 9, or 'casting out nines' as it is otherwise known. Suppose, for example, you see the number 83725163 (which is a very long car registration) and you start to sum its digits from the left. When you add 8 to 3 you get 11, but you must take it to be 2 since $11 \equiv 2 \pmod 9$. You have reduced 11 to 2, modulo 9, by casting out a nine. Now adding this 2 to the next digit, 7, gives 9, but reducing

In Code

modulo 9 it becomes 0. You have just cast out another nine. Now you can start again at the digit 2, and add it to the next digit, 5, to get 7, and add this to 1 to get 8. Then add this 8 to 6 to get 5. (Why?) Finally you add this 5 to 3 to get 8. You conclude that $83725163 \equiv 8 \,(\text{mod}\,9)$. Since this remainder is not 0 you now know that the integer 83725163 is not divisible by 9.

You can take all sorts of liberties when you are determining $s\,\text{mod}\,9$, as shown in the following variation of the calculation just described:

$$
\begin{aligned}
s &= 8 + 3 + 7 + 2 + 5 + 1 + 6 + 3 \\
&= (8 + 3) + (7 + 2) + (5 + 1) + (6 + 3) \\
&\equiv 2 + 0 + 6 + 0\,(\text{mod}\,9) \\
\Rightarrow s &\equiv 8\,(\text{mod}\,9) \\
\Rightarrow s\,\text{mod}\,9 &= 8
\end{aligned}
$$

There are many rules known for deciding whether or not an integer is divisible by small integers such as 4, 7 and 11, to name but a few, but none is as simple or as elegant as the one relating to divisibility by 9. The one that tells when an integer is divisible by 11 is fairly easy to describe but I would rather show a more 'worldly' application of the modulus 11.

Book Numbering

Every modern book carries a 10-digit number on its back cover, normally near the bottom right-hand corner. This is true of the hardback edition of this book, which carries the ten-digit number 1 86197 222 9. This number is this book's ISBN (International Standard Book Number). Its first nine digits are 'information digits' because they code information about the book; in this case the first digit 1 identifies the book as being published in an English-speaking country, the next eight digits identify among other things the publishing house. The tenth and final digit is known as a *check digit* and though, in general, it is redundant in the information sense, it is very useful in checking whether or not a purported ISBN number is

116

a valid one.

Apparently the two types of error most commonly committed by humans when transcribing long strings of digits are a single transcription error in any position, and an error due to the transposition of any two digits.

If an error of either of these types occurs during the transcription, then the tenth digit calculated by a recipient of this supposed ISBN will not match the tenth digit of the submitted number. If the recipient were a bookseller, for example, time would be wasted in a book search that used an invalid ISBN. Let me describe to you how this check digit is calculated, without explaining why computing it in this way provides a 'flag' for the presence of one of the errors just mentioned.

The first information digit is multiplied by 1 (not very difficult), the second by 2, the third by 3, and so on, the ninth digit being multiplied by 9. The results of all these multiplications are added up to get what is known as *the weighted check sum*, S, say. Then the tenth check digit is taken to be $S \bmod 11$. That's all there is to it (which is not quite true because you can take some short cuts in calculating S).

To calculate the check digit in the ISBN for the book whose first nine information digits are 1 86197 222, compute

$$\begin{aligned} S &= (1 \times \mathbf{1}) + (2 \times \mathbf{8}) + (3 \times \mathbf{6}) + (4 \times \mathbf{1}) + (5 \times \mathbf{9}) + (6 \times \mathbf{7}) \\ &\quad + (7 \times \mathbf{2}) + (8 \times \mathbf{2}) + (9 \times \mathbf{2}) \\ &= 1 + 16 + 18 + 4 + 45 + 42 + 14 + 16 + 18 \\ &= 174 \end{aligned}$$

Then $S \bmod 11 = 9$, since $174 = 15 \times 11 + 9$. Appending the check digit 9 to the nine information digits gives the ISBN as 1 86197 222 9.

The use of the modulus 11 in the ISBN scheme is not arbitrary: it exploits the fact that 11 is a prime number. The scheme does not work with 10 as a modulus. Since it is possible to get a remainder of 10 when working with the modulus 11, the letter X is appended instead of the two-digit 10 when this happens, so as to maintain a ten-digit ISBN. *Chamber's Twentieth Century Dictionary*, for example, has the ISBN 0 550 10206 X. The calculation

$$
\begin{aligned}
S &= (1 \times \mathbf{0}) + (2 \times \mathbf{5}) + (3 \times \mathbf{5}) + (4 \times \mathbf{0}) + (5 \times \mathbf{1}) \\
&\quad + (6 \times \mathbf{0}) + (7 \times \mathbf{2}) + (8 \times \mathbf{0}) + (9 \times \mathbf{6}) \\
&\equiv 0 + (-1) + 4 + 0 + 5 + 0 + 3 + 0 + (-1) \ (\mathrm{mod}\,11) \\
\Rightarrow S &\equiv 10\,(\mathrm{mod}\,11) \\
\Rightarrow S\,\mathrm{mod}\,11 &= 10
\end{aligned}
$$

verifies that this is so. Note the clever short cuts based on casting out 11's and using negative numbers (e.g. -1 instead of 10 and 54) to keep computation to a minimum.

Fermat's Little Theorem

The name Fermat has become known to many who might otherwise never have heard of him through Simon Singh's book *Fermat's Last Theorem*. Its main story is how the mathematician Andrew Wiles proved this famous 350-year-old result in 1994. The adjective 'Last' was used because this conjecture was the last of Fermat's many assertions that mathematicians had still not verified. His other statements about natural numbers – and there were many – were in the course of time proved to be true, with the exception of just a few, which were shown by counter-examples to be false. However, this old chestnut defeated the best attempts of the greatest mathematicians over the centuries until at last the Englishman (who had been captivated from childhood by the problem) devoted almost eight years, locked away in his attic, to proving it true.

But Fermat is also known for a theorem which is called *Fermat's Little Theorem* or FLT for short. Whereas the Last Theorem could be described as a negative result in that it states that something can never happen, the FLT is a real extrovert in that it makes very positive assertions. It is also a great theorem and, in stark contrast to the Last Theorem, is much easier to prove. Dad

Sums with a Difference

showed us a gem of a proof, due to a mathematician named James Ivory, dating from 1801.

Fermat is known to have written at some time or other:

> And perhaps posterity will thank me for having shown it that the ancients did not know everything.

Well, the mathematicians of antiquity did not know this result, and posterity is grateful to him for it. Like a lot of mathematical work which seems to have no 'practical application' at the time of its creation, the FLT of 1640, along with a generalisation of it due to Euler in 1736, became of central practical importance much later when, in 1977, it played a vital part in establishing the soundness of the RSA public key cryptosystem.

The historical chain

$$\text{Fermat} \xrightarrow{} \text{Euler} \xrightarrow{} \text{Rivest, Shamir and Adelman}$$
$$1640 \qquad\qquad 1736 \qquad\qquad\qquad 1977$$

links different times and different people, and shows how mathematicians build on previous results.

So what does the FLT say ?

Fermat's Little Theorem: If p is *any* prime number, then

$$a^{p-1} \equiv 1 \,(\mathrm{mod}\, p)$$

for every natural number a relatively prime to p.

Before I say another word, let us choose the prime p to be the number 5. Since $p - 1 = 4$, the FLT says, in this specific case, that

$$a^4 \equiv 1 \,(\mathrm{mod}\, 5)$$

for every natural number a relatively prime to 5.

119

Recall that two natural numbers are relatively prime to each other if (and only if) the only factor they have in common is 1. Which natural numbers a are relatively prime to 5? First, each of the numbers 1, 2, 3 and 4. However, the number 5 shares the factor 5 with itself, so is not relatively prime to itself. OK, so 5 cannot be an a-number. The numbers 6, 7, 8 and 9 are each relatively prime to 5, but 10 is not, because 10 and 5 share the factor 5. The numbers 11, 12, 13 and 14 are also relatively prime to 5, but 15 is not, because 15 and 5 share the factor 5.

I hear you yelling, "Stop! The only numbers which are not relatively prime to 5 are the multiples of 5."

"Yes, the numbers 5, 10, 15, 20, ... are the only ones sharing a factor other than 1 with 5."

So we may say that

$$a^4 \equiv 1 \,(\mathrm{mod}\, 5)$$

for every natural number a not a multiple of 5. So the theorem asserts that

$$1^4 \equiv 1 \,(\mathrm{mod}\, 5)$$
$$2^4 \equiv 1 \,(\mathrm{mod}\, 5)$$
$$3^4 \equiv 1 \,(\mathrm{mod}\, 5)$$
$$4^4 \equiv 1 \,(\mathrm{mod}\, 5)$$
$$6^4 \equiv 1 \,(\mathrm{mod}\, 5)$$
$$7^4 \equiv 1 \,(\mathrm{mod}\, 5)$$
$$8^4 \equiv 1 \,(\mathrm{mod}\, 5)$$
$$9^4 \equiv 1 \,(\mathrm{mod}\, 5)$$
$$11^4 \equiv 1 \,(\mathrm{mod}\, 5)$$

$$\cdot$$
$$\cdot$$
$$\cdot$$

The dots at the end of this array signify that the columns go on for ever in this manner. The only values of a which do not appear are the multiples of 5. For example, there isn't an entry asserting that

Sums with a Difference

$20^4 \equiv 1 \pmod 5$, which is just as well because this is not a true statement. Thus the FLT makes an awful lot of assertions for just one prime. Let's verify some of them.

The first assertion is trivially true as it says that $1 \equiv 1 \pmod 5$: a number is always congruent to itself no matter what the modulus. Is it true that

$$2^4 \equiv 1 \pmod 5?$$

Yes. The assertion that $2^4 \equiv 1 \pmod 5$ means that 5 divides the difference $2^4 - 1$. This is true because $2^4 - 1 = 16 - 1 = 15 = 3 \times 5$. Is this next statement true?

$$3^4 \equiv 1 \pmod 5$$

It is, because $3^4 \equiv 1 \pmod 5$ means that $5 \mid 3^4 - 1 = 80$.

Since, for example, $3^4 \equiv 1 \pmod 5$ is equivalent to saying that $5 \mid 3^4 - 1$, let us rewrite the above assertions in this form. Here is the previous array in different clothes:

$$5 \mid 1^4 - 1$$
$$5 \mid 2^4 - 1$$
$$5 \mid 3^4 - 1$$
$$5 \mid 4^4 - 1$$
$$5 \mid 6^4 - 1$$
$$5 \mid 7^4 - 1$$
$$5 \mid 8^4 - 1$$
$$5 \mid 9^4 - 1$$
$$5 \mid 11^4 - 1$$

$$\cdot$$
$$\cdot$$
$$\cdot$$

To verify these statements we need to show that each of these 'differences' is a multiple of 5. In this case, all we need to do is show that they end in either a 0 or a 5. Here are the results:

In Code

$$1^4 - 1 = 0 = 0 \times 5$$
$$2^4 - 1 = 15 = 3 \times 5$$
$$3^4 - 1 = 80 = 16 \times 5$$
$$4^4 - 1 = 255 = 51 \times 5$$
$$6^4 - 1 = 1295 = 259 \times 5$$
$$7^4 - 1 = 2400 = 480 \times 5$$
$$8^4 - 1 = 4085 = 819 \times 5$$
$$9^4 - 1 = 6560 = 1312 \times 5$$
$$11^4 - 1 = 14640 = 2928 \times 5$$

.
.
.

Why don't you test out the FLT for the prime $p = 7$?

Since the natural numbers a which are relatively prime to a prime number p are precisely those natural numbers which are not multiples of p, the general FLT may be stated in the form:

If p is *any* prime number then

$$a^{p-1} \equiv 1 \,(\mathrm{mod}\,p)$$

for every natural number a that is not a multiple of p.

It may also be written without the use of the congruence notation in the form

$$p \,|\, a^{p-1} - 1$$

for every natural number a that is not a multiple of p.

The FLT is a deep result. It makes an infinite number of statements with regard to each prime. Since there are an infinite number of primes, it makes 'a lot' of statements, all of which are true. Let's look at some of the consequences of this wonderful theorem.

122

Sums with a Difference

An Ancient Chinese Belief (fifth century BC)

The ancient Chinese believed that

$$\text{if } n \text{ is a prime then } n \mid 2^{n-1} - 1$$

and conversely that

$$\text{if } n \mid 2^{n-1} - 1 \text{ then } n \text{ is a prime}$$

(A small point: the prime must be odd, which is the case for all primes except 2.)

What is being said? The first statement says, in words, that if n is a prime, then it *always* divides evenly into $2^{n-1} - 1$. For example, because 7 is a prime it must be that 7 divides evenly into $2^{6-1} - 1 = 63$. It does.

The second statement says, in words, that if n divides evenly into $2^{n-1} - 1$, then n is a prime.

So, for example, if n is the composite number 8, could it be that 8 divides evenly into $2^{7-1} - 1 = 127$? Not according to this statement. If 8 did divide evenly into 127 (which it doesn't), this would mean that 8 is a prime number. So this second statement can be viewed as saying that if n is a composite number then n *never* divides evenly into $2^{n-1} - 1$.

These two statements are often written jointly as

$$n \text{ is prime} \quad \text{if and only if} \quad n \mid 2^{n-1} - 1$$

Were the ancient Chinese right?

The first statement that if n is a prime then $n \mid 2^{n-1} - 1$ is true. Why? Because it's equivalent to the assertion that if n is prime, then

$$2^{n-1} \equiv 1 \pmod{n}$$

This is just the FLT with $p = n$ and $a = 2$. (Since n is odd, 2 is relatively prime to it.)

In Code

So they were right in this regard. You could say that they knew the FLT for the case $a = 2$. Fermat's result is much stronger because it says that when n is a prime, a can be *any* number other than a multiple of n.

However the second statement

$$\text{if } n\,|\,2^{n-1} - 1 \text{ then } n \text{ must be a prime}$$

is false, in general. Amazingly, it is true for all the 271 composite numbers up to and including 340. So the ancient Chinese were right in asserting that if n is one of these composite numbers, then it *never* divides evenly into $2^{n-1} - 1$. None of the composite numbers n less than or equal to 340 makes $2^{n-1} \equiv 1\,(\mathrm{mod}\,n)$. Here are some examples for composite numbers n in this range:

$$2^3 \equiv 0\,(\mathrm{mod}\,4)$$
$$2^{17} \equiv 14\,(\mathrm{mod}\,18)$$
$$2^{44} \equiv 31\,(\mathrm{mod}\,45)$$
$$2^{99} \equiv 88\,(\mathrm{mod}\,100)$$
$$2^{160} \equiv 156\,(\mathrm{mod}\,161)$$
$$2^{215} \equiv 176\,(\mathrm{mod}\,216)$$
$$2^{339} \equiv 8\,(\mathrm{mod}\,340)$$

Notice that none of the numbers to the right of the $\equiv$ symbols is a 1. The ancient Chinese believed that the number 1 never appears on this side if n is composite. However, in 1820 someone discovered (how, I don't know) that for the composite number $341 = 11 \times 33$, it happens that

$$2^{340} \equiv 1\ (\mathrm{mod}\,341)$$

or equivalently that $341\,|\,2^{340} - 1$. This was no mean feat considering that the number $2^{340} - 1$ is an integer consisting of 2860 digits. Of course, the discoverer *did not* write out this monster number in full and painstakingly divide it by 341 to find that 341 divided into it evenly. We'll show how this can be done quite easily

124

Sums with a Difference

in a moment.

This unwelcome fact destroys another beautiful hypothesis. Had the Chinese been right, the fact that $341 \mid 2^{340} - 1$ would prove that 341 is a prime. Unfortunately, it is not. The number $n = 341$ is the *first* counter-example to the conjecture that

$$n \mid 2^{n-1} - 1 \Rightarrow n \text{ an odd prime}$$

Considering the enormity of the number $2^{340} - 1$, and the fact that the conjecture holds for 271 composite numbers less than 341, it is not hard to see why the ancient Chinese were led to believe what they did. This example serves as another lesson that one cannot argue from the 'particular to the general'. Although all the swans I have ever seen were white, it is not true that all swans are white. To establish a general result you have to be able to supply a proof that covers all cases.

It would have been truly great had the ancient Chinese been completely right in what they asserted. Why? Because it would have been a criterion for deciding whether a (large) natural number n is prime. Were it true, it would say, "Compute the residue $2^{n-1} - 1 \bmod n$. If it comes out to be 1, then n is prime, if not, then n is composite". Alas!

Important Remark: It is simple to compute $b^{n-1} \bmod n$ for any natural number b using an algorithm known as the *fast exponentiation algorithm* (FEA), which is based on *repeated squaring*. We don't need to know how it works, only that it requires no more than minutes on an ordinary computer to compute $b^{n-1} \bmod n$ for an n with several thousands digits.

So how did our nineteenth-century mystery person twig that $341 \mid 2^{340} - 1$? I don't know, but perhaps (s)he noticed that

$$2^{10} = 1024 = 3 \times 341 + 1$$

so that $2^{10} - 1 = 3 \times 341$. This says that $341 \mid 2^{10} - 1$, or

125

equivalently that

$$2^{10} \equiv 1 \pmod{341}$$

From this observation it follows, on raising both sides of this congruence to the power 34, that

$$2^{340} \equiv 1 \pmod{341}$$

Game, set and match. Thus $341 \mid 2^{340} - 1$. A pity.

Pseudoprimes

If it were the case that

$$2^{340} \equiv 5 \pmod{341}$$

then we would know immediately that 341 is a composite number.

Why again, exactly? Because if 341 were a prime, the FLT would assert that

$$2^{340} \equiv 1 \pmod{341}$$

Then $2^{340} \equiv 5 \pmod{341}$ would reveal 341 as a composite immediately.

However, the fact that $2^{340} \equiv 1 \pmod{341}$ does not prove that 341 is prime. We say that the integer 341 passes the 'FLT test for the base 2', but we cannot, as a result of this one test, say that 341 is prime. If 341 were prime, the FLT would also assert (because 3 is relatively prime to 341) that $3^{340} \equiv 1 \pmod{341}$.

This is where 341 is revealed to be composite. The fast exponentiation algorithm shows in a jiffy that

$$3^{340} \equiv 56 \pmod{341}$$

Sums with a Difference

Now we know that 341 is composite. This result unmasks the composite nature of 341. The number 3 is said to be a *witness* to the compositeness of 341. It is worth thinking about what is taking place here.

A number (acting as modulus) which passes the FLT for a given integer a, but which is not a prime, is said to be a *pseudoprime to the base a*. Because 341 passes the FLT test for the number 2, the number 341 is a pseudoprime to the base 2. However, the number 341 is not a pseudoprime to the base 3. You might like to know that the composite number $91 = 7 \times 13$ is a pseudoprime to the base 3 because

$$3^{90} \equiv 1 \pmod{91}$$

Something very important and striking has just occurred. Because

$$3^{340} \equiv 56 \pmod{341}$$

we can say with certainty that 341 is a composite number. We are saying with certainty, *without* displaying a single (non-trivial) factor to support our claim, that 341 is composite.

If you are not impressed by that example, consider this one. Using the FEA it is simple to show quickly for the number 2, which is obviously relatively prime to 11111, that

$$2^{11110} \equiv 10536 \pmod{11111}$$

Thus we can say with complete confidence that 11111 is a composite number. Simply amazing! And we haven't displayed a single factor. Can you find two non-trivial factors of 11111?

I have used the words 'interesting' and 'fascinating' many times up to this point (I checked – 'interesting' eleven times and 'fascinating' three times!). But nowhere could they be used with more justification than now.

The only way we have so far seen of knowing that a number is composite was by displaying a (non-trivial) factor. But there is another way. It is a major new insight into the nature of composite

127

numbers to realise that the FLT can (sometimes) reveal the compositeness of a number n without exhibiting a single factor. To reiterate how it achieves this, if

$$a^{n-1} \not\equiv 1 \, (\bmod \, n)$$

for some a, then n is composite.

There are 'large' numbers known to be composite in just this way, yet no one knows any of their non-trivial factors.

The Parting of the Problems

Suppose we take an integer n and start 'testing' it by calculating a^{n-1} for $a = 2, 3, 4, \ldots$, reducing modulo n, and suppose that on each occasion it happens that $a^{n-1} \equiv 1 \, (\bmod \, n)$. What can we say? Unfortunately, we cannot conclude that, just because n has passed the FLT for this number of 'bases', the integer n is prime. It may well be, and probably is, but we cannot be sure. Using this method we would need to test every base up to $a = n - 1$, and only then, if each base has passed the FLT test, could we with certainty pronounce n to be prime. This is clearly a totally inefficient way of testing that the integer n is prime, and is even worse than the trial division algorithm.

However, you'd be forgiven for thinking that if n is composite, then some small base a will make $a^{n-1} \not\equiv 1 \, (\bmod \, n)$ and so reveal n as a composite very quickly. You might also be forgiven for thinking that if this does not happen for the first ten bases, say, then n is almost certainly a prime. Alas, neither is the case. There are composite numbers n which pass the FLT test for every base number relatively prime to n. They are called *Carmichael numbers* because they were discovered by a mathematician of that name in 1912. It is known (since 1996) that there are an infinite number of them, which is very sad from the point of view of establishing compositeness using the FLT test. The smallest of the species is $n = 561$. Every a relatively prime to 561 makes $a^{n-1} \equiv 1 \, (\bmod \, n)$, though $561 = 3 \times$

Sums with a Difference

11×17 is composite. Here the base $a = 3$ would show that $a^{560} \not\equiv 1 \pmod{561}$ and so reveal this number to be composite with just two tests. However, not all Carmichael numbers have a small factor, so testing in this manner could prove very inefficient.

Nevertheless, there are refinements of the FLT test which declare very quickly whether Carmichael numbers are composite. If an integer n has not been shown to be composite after undergoing several such tests, then it is classified as a probable prime, though it would not actually have been proved to be prime. These so-called Monte Carlo tests which produce probable primes are very fast and, while not providing certainty, can reduce the probability that the integer is not a prime below the probability of my winning the National Lottery two weeks running.

There are tests, termed *deterministic primality tests*, which establish prime numbers to be so with certainty. They are slower than the tests which produce primes with a high degree of certainty, but many, known since the late 1980s, can provide proof of primality for integers in excess of 500 digits in a matter of minutes. This is an extremely important practical fact because many modern cryptosystems rely fundamentally on the use of prime numbers of 100 digits or more.

Because of the FLT test and its refinements, we can determine quite quickly whether or not an integer of some hundreds of digits is a prime. The problem of factorising a known composite number with the same number of digits is considered much harder. It is crucial to understand that deciding whether an integer n is prime or composite is different from finding the factors of a random large composite integer. Because the trial division algorithm either tells that a number is prime or produces a factor of a composite integer, we are inclined to view both problems as being one and the same. It can take time to appreciate that testing for primality and providing a factorisation are two separate problems; the first being relatively easy while the second is currently believed – though not proven – to be intractable.

The FLT depends vitally on the fact that the modulus p is a prime number. It is another striking example of the elite role that

In Code

primes play among the natural numbers. If you try the FLT for a composite n, you'll find it won't work. For example, try $n = 8$ and $a = 3$. Does $8 \mid 3^7 - 1$? It doesn't, because $3^7 - 1 = 2187 - 1 = 2186$, which is not divisible by 8.

Leonhard Euler was the first to investigate the more general case where n is any natural number. He eventually found the answer in 1736. His result is slightly more technical than the FLT but this is offset by the fact that it is more general, applying as it does to every natural number n. It is discussed in Appendix D.

Other Excursions

The mathematics just described deals almost exclusively with whole numbers or integers. The area of study devoted to discovering their properties is renowned for being very difficult. Despite this, it has captivated the minds of some of the greatest mathematicians over the ages. There are numbers 'beyond' the integers, the simplest and most familiar of which are the fractions. In case you have forgotten, a fraction has a *numerator* and a *denominator*. The numerator of the fraction $5/13$ is 5, while its denominator is 13. The fraction $5/13$ can be expressed in ratio form as $5 : 13$. So, speaking a little loosely, you could say that fractions are expressible as the ratio of two whole numbers. For this reason they are often called *rational* numbers, or rationals for short. Thus $1/2$ and $-3/4$ are rational numbers though they are not integers. Integers, on the other hand, are rational numbers because they can be thought of as fractions whose denominators are 1.

For a long time it was believed that there were no types of number other than rationals. The ancient Pythagorean proclamation that 'all is number' was an expression of this belief. But there are other species of number. Beyond the rationals are the *real numbers*, including such wonders as $\sqrt{2}$, the golden ratio ϕ, the base of the natural logarithms e and, of course, the ubiquitous π. These numbers, some of which, as you can see, have letters for their names, are considered 'real' because they convince us of their existence by being geometrical ratios or other tangible quantities. There are also numbers which are not 'real', known as *complex numbers* and built around the mysterious $\sqrt{-1}$.

Unfortunately all these exotic numbers play no part in the tale to be told so I must refrain from digressing for a couple of hundred pages to tell you 'all' about them – not that I could. However, I cannot resist saying just a little about some of them.

Dad gave one three-hour lecture (less twenty minutes for a tea break) on the four numbers $\sqrt{2}$, ϕ, e and π. I had some inkling that π is an interesting number, I had never heard of e, and I thought I had heard about ϕ but I was mistaken. I fancied that there was nothing much to be said about $\sqrt{2}$, other than saying that it's that number which when squared gives 2. Of course, I should have known better! I was to learn that there is much, of an elementary nature, that can be said about $\sqrt{2}$. It was with its very definition that we started our excursion, teasing out what is really meant by it. We learned how upset the Greeks were first when they realised the 'different' nature of this number – upset to the point, apparently, of drowning some poor devil just because he blabbed that all was not well with the accepted dogma that every positive number could be expressed as a ratio of two natural numbers.

The number $\sqrt{2}$ makes its presence felt by being the length of the diagonal of a square whose side measures one unit in length. Ironically, it is the famous theorem of Pythagoras that tells us this. So what is new or different about $\sqrt{2}$? Well, try as they might the Greeks couldn't find a rational number which when squared gave 2 exactly. No approximations, like 17/12 (which incidentally doesn't do too bad a job), would do. No sir! It was to be all or nothing:

WANTED

A fraction whose square is 2·00000000000000000...
with 0's all the way 'to infinity'.

They never found one. Being clever fellows, it gradually dawned on them that perhaps there is no such fraction, but how could they possibly prove such a thing? Well, I won't go on about it, but as you

In Code

have probably guessed they did finally (about three hundred years after first suspecting that there was more to $\sqrt{2}$ than meets the eye) find an argument which showed beyond doubt that *there is no fraction which when squared gives 2*. So $\sqrt{2}$ was a new specimen.

The proof that $\sqrt{2}$ is irrational (*not* expressible as a ratio of two whole numbers) so enthralled the English mathematician G. H. Hardy (1877–1947) as a boy that from the moment he read it, he decided to devote his life to mathematics. He did, and he became one of England's greatest mathematicians. He wrote a book called *A Mathematician's Apology*. It was Hardy who said "Beauty is the first test. There is no permanent place in the world for ugly mathematics." The proof that $\sqrt{2}$ is irrational is another of those proofs by contradiction. It's a classic.

Dad showed us how the ancient Babylonians obtained a formula for finding rational approximations to $\sqrt{2}$ which is equivalent to one that was obtained later (after 1700) using a procedure known as Newton's method. He also showed how to derive the next term in the sequence

$$\frac{1}{1}, \frac{3}{2}, \frac{7}{5}, \frac{17}{12}, \frac{41}{29}, \frac{99}{70}, \dots$$

The successive terms of this sequence give better and better fractional approximations to $\sqrt{2}$. Try a few on a calculator and see. Just divide the numerator by the denominator and square the result. Have another look at the fractions above to see how you might get the next one from the previous one before reading on.

> To get the denominator of the next term in the sequence you simply add the denominator and numerator of the previous fraction, while to get the numerator you simply add twice the denominator of the previous fraction to its numerator.

Let's see how $7/5$ generates the next fraction according to this procedure. The new denominator is $5 + 7 = 12$, while the new numerator is $2 \times 5 + 7 = 17$. So the next fraction should be $17/12$. It is.

Sums with a Difference

Dad showed us some consequences of the irrationality of $\sqrt{2}$ which I found startling but which gave me a deeper insight into what it meant to be irrational (!). The side of a square and its diagonal cannot both be measured exactly with the same ruler no matter how fine its markings. Can you believe that? A fancy way of putting this is to say that the side and diagonal of a square are *incommensurable*. If you have a ruler which measures the side exactly (meaning that the two end points of the side coincide with two markings of the ruler), then that same ruler when placed along the diagonal so that one of its markings coincides with the initial point of the diagonal, will have the end point of the diagonal lying between two of its markings. Always. And if the ruler measures the diagonal exactly it will fail to measure the side exactly. If you had at your disposal a new ruler with ultra-close markings, or even an infinity of such rulers with every conceivable separation between the markings, it would make no difference. This geometrical fact gave me more respect for $\sqrt{2}$ – it held some interest.

Dad gave a two-dimensional example of a rectangle in which the lengths of the longer and shorter sides are in the ratio $\sqrt{2}:1$. This rectangle cannot be tiled with square tiles, no matter how small the tiles. We have all seen rectangles which are approximately this shape. If you have an A4 pad of paper close by, look at its cover on which it says that the pad measures 297×210 mm. Now, the last fraction in the sequence mentioned above is $99/70$. Multiply it 'above and below' by 3 to get $297/210$. The A4 sheet is supposed to have the length of its longer to its shorter side in the *exact* ratio $\sqrt{2}:1$ for a very practical reason. In this case (and in this case only, as a little algebra easily shows), the sheet can be folded along its longer side to give two smaller rectangles, for each of which the ratio of the longer to the shorter side is again $\sqrt{2}:1$. Thus each of the new sheets thus formed has the same property as the parent. Two A4 sheets are the offspring of a single A3, and in turn, two A3's come from one A2. The first in the line of the A series is an A0 sheet whose dimensions are 1189×841 mm. This is approximately a square metre in area. Fold an A4 page in two and check that the ratio of the longer to the shorter side is approximately $\sqrt{2}:1$.

In Code

Of the other three numbers, φ, e and π, much was said about φ but all that I remember now is something about a golden rectangle and a mention of the Fibonacci sequence. Most of what I heard about the number e has also receded into the memory's mists, but I have a faint recollection of a bank manager who was willing to pay 100 per cent interest per annum on an investment of £1. He was also willing to have interest added every six months at 50 per cent compound interest, or even to have interest compounded every day at the appropriate rate. He was even willing to be pushed to the limits of his resources and his generosity and allow the £1 to gather interest 'continuously'. I also remember that even with all this frantic adding of interest, the £1 does not exceed all known fortunes by the end of a year. Instead it becomes a modest £2·72. The decimal 2·72 is the number e = 2·718281 ... rounded to two decimal places. (By the way, the letter e is used in honour of Euler.)

As for our old school chum π, the latest is that its decimal expansion is now known to 206158430000 digits.

We covered many other interesting topics in the Mathematical Excursions evening class. One was floors and ceilings (nothing to do with building); another was magic squares and knights hopping all around the chessboard. (Speaking of which, I bet you think that there are 64 squares on the chessboard. Well, there are 204. How about that?) A further topic was quadratics and projectiles, while in another, a ball was dropping from far up in the sky and we were trying to figure out how fast it was going at any given instant – instantaneous speed. Calculus stuff.

But Dad was at his most dramatic when we discussed probability. This was then I realised that he was a closet gambler, if not a latent conman. During these talks, packs of cards, dice and other miscellaneous props such as toy cars and large mugs made their appearance. There was talk of winning lotteries, fellows getting on planes with bombs, birthday paradoxes, goats and cars behind screens, envelopes with sums of money in them, buying cornflakes boxes to collect models of Robin Hood and his Merry Men and, of course, playing poker.

He revelled in confounding our intuitions with bizarre

examples. At one stage he showed us three cards, one coloured red on both sides, another coloured blue on both sides and the other coloured red on one side and blue on the other. "If you choose a card from one of these three and it's red on one side, what would you bet me that the other side is blue?" Don't be fooled! It's not a fifty-fifty bet (to use bookmakers' language).

We discussed decision-making based on assessments of probabilities, when to play and when to fold in poker games. We saw counter-intuitive card tricks, such as the one just described, and of course we discussed Monty's game show with the aforementioned car and goats. This amazing problem appears in almost every modern popular book on mathematics and there are great stories connected with it, some of which are discussed at length in the book *The Man Who Loved Only Numbers* – a biography of the Hungarian mathematician Paul Erdös.

Now that 1 have almost surely whetted your appetite, it would be cruel of me not to state the problem. Here goes. A car is hidden behind one of three doors, and each of the other two doors conceals a goat. Lucky you, who gets to guess where the car is, choose door 1. Monty, the game show host, who knows where the car is, then opens one of the other two doors to reveal a goat. He asks you whether or not you wish to switch from your original choice of door to the other closed door. Should you switch? (The all-important answer, along with a brief explanation, is given in Appendix B).

5. One Way Only

Dad began one of our excursions into cryptography by saying that a fascinating aspect of the modern form of the science is that things which appear to be of a negative nature are exploited in a positive way. He hoped to illustrate this point by telling us about one-way functions and one-way trapdoor functions. The word 'trapdoor' caught my attention immediately, and I wondered how such a term could be used in relation to functions. 'One-way' conjured up an image of one-way streets. So already I was sure I was going to enjoy this lecture, though I was hoping it wouldn't get too technical. You know how it sometimes happens – you follow everything for the first ten-minutes and then you wonder at what point the lecturer started talking double Dutch. Dad continued by saying that after he had described the nature of these 'wonderful' functions we would probably ask him, "What possible use could anyone make of these?" In order to whet our appetites – and to ensure that we would listen attentively – he said, "Let me tell you about a little problem that Alice and Bob had which they solved using one-way functions."

Alice and Bob work for the same company, a very prestigious computer company. They are both managers at the same grade, Alice in London and Bob in New York. The company has a very important upcoming conference in Tokyo which they would both love to attend. Unfortunately, the company is willing to provide an all-expenses-paid trip for just one of them, and has left it up to them to decide which will go. So now we see the cause of their concern.

If Alice and Bob were in the same place they could decide the

136

matter in the time-honoured fashion by tossing a coin, but they are not. But the amazing thing is that they can simulate the fair toss of a coin. "How could they possibly do such a thing?" I hear you ask. Answer – by using a one-way function. The procedure they use is known as the *remote coin-tossing protocol*. When I first heard mention of this I was intrigued and captivated. Who gets to toss the coin, and how can the other person be sure that (s)he is not being cheated?

To describe to you how the two executives settled matters, I must begin by telling you about one-way functions. Strictly speaking, these are mathematical functions or transformations, but we can describe a one-way function loosely as an operation that is easy to do but extremely difficult, if not impossible, to undo.

For example, it is easy to mix a can of white paint with a can of black to obtain a mixture of grey, but none of us would relish the task of having to recover the original measures of white and black paint. It is easy to go one way, to do the mixing, but to reverse this process and undo the mixing is nigh on impossible. It is easy to squeeze toothpaste out of the tube, but how would you get it to go back in? The good cup or dish that is all too easily broken into pieces is rarely recoverable. Humpty Dumpty was a victim of this element of irreversibility when he had his great fall off the wall, for

> All the King's horses and all the King's men
> Couldn't put Humpty together again.

Not all examples of one-way functions are so strongly suggestive of order descending into chaos without any hope of redemption. If you have a person's name and address it is easy to look up their telephone number in a telephone book. Suppose, on the other hand, that you were at a party many weeks ago and had jotted down on a slip of paper someone's telephone number but have now forgotten its owner's name. If you would dearly like to know who the person is then you are in a pickle. Unless you are willing to risk giving offence by dialing the number without any idea of who it is you might be phoning, you may as well regard yourself as being on the reverse side of a one-way function. Whereas it is easy to find a telephone number corresponding to a name, it is a horse of a different colour – given the construction of normal telephone directories – to find a name corresponding to a number. If you were desperate (and you would certainly need to be) you could work your way down the columns of numbers in what you hope is the appropriate directory until you find the number which will reveal the name you're after. The fact that it is not impossible, even if it is prohibitively time-consuming, to recover the name from the number is what makes this example of a one-way function more interesting and close to the kind of one-way function that cryptographers exploit. If you had a special directory which lists telephone numbers in numerical order and gives the corresponding names (these directories are not available to the general public, who would have little use for them), then the job of finding the name from the number is no more difficult than the other way round. This special information, often glamorously referred to as 'trapdoor' information, effectively undoes the one-way function. (More on this later.)

Here is another example. John and Heidi become the best of friends at summer camp. When Heidi returns to Germany, John, in order to impress his new-found friend, takes out his English–German dictionary and attempts to write a letter in German which he then sends to Heidi. A few days later a reply arrives from Heidi written in German. John, who knows only a little German, is unable to translate most of Heidi's words and is beside himself with curiosity as to their meaning. His own dictionary is not of much use to him: it is a one-way dictionary – English into German – and not, as he now needs, German into English. This situation is the same as the telephone directory with names corresponding to English words and numbers corresponding to German words. John has lots of numbers for which he desperately wants names. Nothing for it but to go out and buy a German–English dictionary, which, he is pleased to find, he can do. It is not always so easy to find the trapdoor.

Let me give an example with numbers which illustrates clearly

One Way Only

the key idea of 'easy one way, hard the other way' that is central to the notion of a one-way function. (Don't worry, I haven't forgotten about Alice and Bob, but it will be a while before I get back to them.)

Choose two prime numbers, p and q say, each five or six digits long, from a book of primes and multiply them on your calculator to obtain their product, n. Give the calculator with the number n displayed on it to a friend. Tell him how n was formed and challenge him to use the calculator to find p and q. (Unique factorisation guarantees that n can be recovered only by discovering p and q.) Don't hold your breath while waiting for the answer.

Here, the forward operation of *multiplying* is computationally easy, whereas the backward operation of *factorising* is computationally hard. You, who know how n was computed in the first instance, are in possession of the secret trapdoor information – the factorisation of n into its factors p and q.

Of course, if you allow your friend to use a computer equipped with a factorisation algorithm then he will find p and q in a short while, because the primes you chose are relatively small and current factorisation techniques will be adequate to the task. But up the ante, and use the very same computer to choose two very large prime numbers, say of a hundred digits each (that this can be done is a story in itself), and form $n = p \times q$ as before. This huge multiplication can be done by a computer in the twinkling of an eye. Now show the product n to your friend and leave him with his super-duper computer to search for p and q. He will not find them.

Here is an actual 200-digit product of two primes p and q:

3158047947602683834343402871132072584715488222894775015428152222808368344736897467605980757546290594836395556373144745242759035196176119637870933244742660580931814608712962665610564695478209228003844 29

Can you find p and q? Do you want to? You may use all the computing power you can get your hands on.

Before I describe how the coin-tossing protocol works and

return to Alice and Bob to see which of them is going to go to Tokyo, let me explain in simple mathematical terms what it means for a function to qualify as a one-way function. First and foremost, it must be a one-to-one function (meaning that corresponding to each y there is a unique x). If you have forgotten about the function notation and all this one-to-one business you could look back to Chapter 3, but really you can read on because you'll get the idea even if you are a little hazy about the notation. One warning, however: since the terms one-to-one and one-way are similar, be on your guard.

Here goes. A function f is a one-way function if

it is easy to compute $y = f(x)$ for each x

but

given y it is very difficult to compute $f^{-1}(y) = x$

All of which is in keeping with our earlier 'easy one way, very hard the other way'.

The function $f(x) = 2x + 1$, which is a one-to-one function, could hardly be described as a one-way function. It is easy to figure out from a given y the unique value of x that generates it. Using algebra,

$$y = 2x + 1 \Rightarrow 2x = y - 1 \Rightarrow x = \frac{y - 1}{2}$$

So this function holds no mystery and does not qualify as a one-way function. On the other hand, the cubing function

$$f(x) = x^3$$

is a little different. If you don't have a calculator or computer, then my telling you that $y = 1860867$ and asking you for the value of x whose cube is this y, might tax your computational abilities. It is not so easy to see how to unravel or invert the action of this cubing function. However, it *can be done*, and in this case you would find that $x = 123$. Although this function would not be regarded as a one-way function, we can see that there is much more to inverting it than there is with $f(x) = 2x + 1$ and we get an inkling of the nature of a one-way function. So to reiterate: a one-way function is one for which it is easy to compute $y = f(x)$, but not so easy, in fact downright hard, to figure out x given $y = f(x)$. If it can be done at all, it simply takes too much time. The phrase used is 'computationally infeasible'. Lots of one-way functions are 'known', though if truth be told nobody has ever given a strict mathematical definition of what is meant by 'hard to invert', and so no one has ever proved that such functions really exist. A good barrister might have a field day cross-examining us on what exactly a one-way function is. But, that said, mathematicians know from centuries of experience that certain mathematical operations are easy to do, but that nobody has ever figured out a smart and efficient way to undo them (in the same way that I can't prove to you there is no easy way to unmix those cans of white and black paint, but I'd be willing to bet you a lot of money that there isn't).

At last we can describe how Alice and Bob settled their difficulty.

A Coin-Tossing Protocol

1. Alice and Bob agree on a one-way function f.
2. Alice chooses a random number x and computes $y = f(x)$.
3. Alice sends y to Bob.
4. Since Bob cannot compute x from a knowledge of y, he simply guesses whether x is even (heads, say) or odd (tails), and relays his guess to Alice. This is the 'coin-toss'.
5. Alice tells Bob whether he won or lost the toss, and then sends x to Bob.
6. Bob confirms the result of the toss by verifying that $y = f(x)$.

The security of this protocol rests on the one-way function. Let us see what this is all about, step by step.

In Code

Step (1) How do Alice and Bob agree on the one-way function f? Well, we are assuming that everything is done by computers which have appropriate mathematical software. Alice has her computer on her desk in London, and Bob has his in New York. Furthermore, they have email facilities so they can communicate with each other. They are mathematically literate so they both know what a one-way function is and have access to any number of such functions. So to begin, Alice chooses a one-way function and sends it to Bob by email for his approval. It is rather like saying, if they were together in the same room, "Are you happy that I toss this particular coin?"

Step (2) Alice chooses a random number x and computes $y = f(x)$. It should be said that the number of choices for x that Alice will have at her disposal will be truly enormous, but it is wise to get the machine to pick one such number from this myriad of possibilities using its random number generator rather than choosing herself. She may, without knowing it, betray certain biases such as favouring even numbers or ones ending in a 3.

Step (3) Alice calculates y by computing $f(x)$. She sends y to Bob but keeps knowledge of x to herself for the moment. This is all very straightforward.

Step (4) So now the number y pops up on Bob's computer screen in New York, and all he has to do is say whether or not the x that generated this y is an odd or even number. This is the coin-toss: odd or even – heads or tails, a fifty-fifty bet. Clearly this is a crucial stage in the protocol. Bob knows the function f and also that $y = f(x)$ for some unknown integer x. Can he deduce what x is from these two facts? No! He has neither the time nor the ability to figure out from this information what x is, because the function f is one of those nasty irreversible functions. This is where the one-way property of f is being set to work. There's nothing for it but simply to guess that x is even, say, relay the guess to Alice and hope for the best.

Step (5) Moments later, "Sorry, Bob! Better luck next time. The

142

number x I chose is odd. I know you trust me, but here is my lucky x anyway."

Step (6) Of course, Bob does not trust Alice, but because she has sent him an x he knows his goose is cooked. He has no doubt that when he applies the f, which he received at the outset from Alice, to x he will get the y that she sent him. This is how he verifies that there have been no shenanigans.

That is the gist of the protocol, which I found truly fascinating when I first heard it described. There are certain questions you might well ask. One is, "Could it be that Alice can have an odd x_{odd} and also an even x_{even}, each of which produces the y that she sends to Bob so that if he guesses odd she swindles him by sending the x_{even} for verification?" No, because the functions used are one-to-one. Bob would know that in addition to being one-way, the function f sent by Alice is such that there is only one x corresponding to y. So that kind of skullduggery is ruled out.

However, there are subtleties and one needs to be vigilant. Suppose the cubing function were truly a one-way function (which it is not), and that Alice unwittingly asked for this to be the function f used as the one-way function for the coin-toss. Bob would be secretly delighted and no doubt agree. When Alice sends him y he knows he cannot compute the x that produces this y – but he doesn't need to. He is simply being asked to say whether x is even or odd. What could you say about the oddness or otherwise of x if you were to receive a y that is even?

So Alice got to go to Tokyo. You didn't think I was going to let the man win, did you?

What I liked about the lecture on one-way functions and their exotic cousins, the one-way trapdoor functions, was that it was for the most part conceptual in nature. There was nothing more technical needed than an elementary knowledge of what is meant by a function and the notation employed, a little about one-to-one-ness and an understanding of a one-way function. It was really about the power of simple ideas which are imaginative and easily grasped. When I said this to Dad he was delighted, telling me that he had read somewhere that the real moving force in mathematics is imagination, that it was a subject full of truly imaginative ideas. He said that the great German mathematician David Hilbert, on being told that some student had forsaken mathematics for poetry, quipped, "It is just as well, he didn't have enough imagination to be a mathematician."

Passwords

One-way functions are used to protect passwords by encrypting them and storing only the enciphered version. This allows a password to be kept absolutely private so that not even the system administrator knows it. When a 'word' is first submitted as a password, the system encrypts it with the one-way function, and places the resulting 'string' of gobbledygook in a file which is called a password file. No record of the word submitted is kept. When the user logs on at future times and enters the password when requested, the *same* one-way function is applied to it and so produces the same ciphertext string as before. The password file is then searched for a matching string, and when it is found access is granted to the system. A very good scheme.

Part of the great story told in Clifford Stoll's book *The Cuckoo's Egg* is an account of how a hacker 'got around' a one-way function and netted a plaintext password. Stoll had been tracking this hacker (called H from now on) for months without H's knowing it. (Read the book, I couldn't put it down.) One night Stoll saw H downloading a password file from a certain Unix machine. (H had figured out how to get into this machine sometime previously.) "Why is H doing this?" Stoll asked himself, wondering what possible good can it do for H to be copying down all this gobbledygook when, surely, H knows that the one-way function guarantees that the strings cannot be decrypted to reveal the corresponding English passwords. So what is afoot?

Three weeks later Stoll sees H back in the same computer

One Way Only

system attempting to log on as a private user. Stoll waits and watches. A password is requested. One is duly entered and H is 'in' – in to someone's private account! What happened? Rest assured that H did not find this password by finding the inverse of the one-way function which would have allowed the password file to be deciphered. Answer: H had a Unix machine which used exactly the same one-way function to encipher passwords. So the clever but devious H, with possibly a lot of help from collaborators, had painstakingly submitted *every* single word from an English Dictionary to this machine as a password and created a file of encrypted passwords, keeping track of the strings generated by each English word. This done, H compared the entries in this file with the one downloaded weeks earlier hoping for a match. The extraordinary pains H had taken paid off. A match was found. H had a (plaintext) password.

Because Stoll alerted the computer world to this possibility, it is now recommended that a password should not be an English word on its own. Should you wish to use some easily remembered word, such as the name of a boat, as was used by one person mentioned in Stoll's book, then use it as part of a longer string of plaintext characters containing numbers and other symbols, preferably interleaved with the English characters. This simple expedient makes the above 'attack' much, much harder. Had this been done by each user at the computer installation penetrated by H, each password would have remained beyond reach.

Where's the Trapdoor?

Now that I knew the idea behind a one-way function I was curious to know what a one-way *trapdoor* function might be. That extra term 'trapdoor', between one-way and function was intriguing. Before telling us, Dad had to do 'the teacher bit' and have us remind him what a one-way function is. So to get things moving, somebody said, "Something which is easy to compute one way but virtually impossible the other way." Well, words to that effect.

145

By way of response Dad said, "Put slightly more technically, if f is a one-way function then it is easy to work out $f(x)$ to get a number y, but if only y is known then it is computationally infeasible to find x."

We know. Forget about trying unless you have a few thousand computers and a lot of time because there isn't a realistic hope of finding x from y. Come on, tell us what a one-way trapdoor function is.

"A one-way trapdoor function is a function which is not a one-way function."

He's not serious, surely? He's expressing himself this way for effect!

"You can't be saying that 'trapdoor' is just a very fancy way of saying not."

"In a sense, yes. A one-way trapdoor function is not a one-way function for the person who dreams it up. For the rest of us, it is still a one-way function and this is all-important."

Curiouser and curiouser!

He continued, "The designer constructs the function in such a way that only he knows how to find x from y, only he knows how to invert the function. This special information, which he keeps to himself, is called the 'trapdoor' information. Apparently this term was inspired by those two-clown stage acts in which one clown pretends to the audience that only he knew where a trapdoor was in the stage floor, while his colleague didn't. When the one ignorant of its existence stood over it, the clown (with the trapdoor information) would have it spring open, and the unfortunate one would disappear down through the floor to howls of laughter."

We have all seen films where the hero, who is being chased by an evil bunch out to capture or kill him, dashes into a library with no exit other than the door he just entered. While we are certain that he is to be caught by his pursuers, who are hot on his heels, he makes towards a book behind which is a mechanism which causes a bookcase to open. He slips quickly through the opening and escapes along a secret passage while the bookcase swings back to its original position. When the villains enter the library moments later, we witness their astonishment at finding no trace of him. Even if one of them is quick-witted enough to guess what must have taken place, we and they know that the there is no hope of finding that special book (which is the hero's trapdoor information) in time to continue the chase.

An American Intellectual Revolution

In 1976, Matrin Hellman and Whitfield Diffie had the imagination and foresight to see how one-way trapdoor functions could revolutionise cryptography. They outlined their wonderful ideas in a paper entitled 'New Directions in Cryptography', and acknowledged independent ideas of Ralph Merkle which appear in his paper 'Secure Communications over Insecure Channels'. So, without further ado, let me tell you something about this new cryptography.

Alice, Bob, Clare, Denis and others each design a one-way trapdoor function. Call the one that Alice designs f_A (read as f sub A). Similarly, let f_B be Bob's one-way trapdoor function, and f_C and f_D the respective one-way trapdoor functions of Clare and Denis. This done, they submit these functions to a public directory along with their names and other relevant information. The table

Public Directory	
Alice	f_A
Bob	f_B
Clare	f_C
Denis	f_D
⋮	⋮

shows names (only) along with the corresponding functions – on display for *all* to see, just like names and numbers in a telephone directory. Except to the person who submitted it, any one of these is a one-way function. This means that no one can figure out in a realistic amount of time, even with unlimited resources, how to

In Code

invert it – no one, that is, other than the person who submitted it to the directory. (S)he (presumably) already knows how to invert this function because (s)he possesses the special trapdoor information which accomplishes this.

Alice, Bob, Clare, Denis and company keep secret the inverse function corresponding to the function which each has made public. Alice keeps knowledge of f_A^{-1} entirely to herself, as does Bob with f_B^{-1} and Clare and Denis with f_C^{-1} and f_D^{-1}. Anyone submitting an f to this public directory *must* keep secret the f^{-1} which undoes the action of f.

So? Well, these public one-way functions can now be used as enciphering transformations to send messages in encrypted form between any or all of the subscribers to this public directory.

For example, if Alice wishes to communicate with Bob, then all she need do is look up Bob's enciphering transformation f_B in the public directory. When she types her message on a computer screen she applies f_B to it and sends it by email to Bob. On receipt of this enciphered email he applies the deciphering transformation f_B^{-1} (which is kept secret on his computer) to decipher the ciphertext and so read Alice's message. Anyone who eavesdrops on this message cannot decipher and read it even if (s)he knows it is intended for Bob.

An important point: Alice doesn't have to know Bob to be able to write to him in secret. This is the same as my looking up the telephone number of someone I don't know personally and phoning him.

Public Key Cryptography

Strictly speaking, it is not the enciphering functions f_A, f_B, f_C and f_D which Alice, Bob, Clare and Denis submit to the public directory, but the keys associated with these functions. By the same token, what they keep secret are the corresponding deciphering keys. In general, each uses the same type of mathematcal function but with an individual enciphering key. Each must keep the corresponding deciphering key absolutely top secret.

This form of cryptography, based as it is on a public directory which contains the enciphering key of each user, is known as *public key cryptography*, and any particular cryptosystem which implements such a scheme is called a *public key system*, or PKS for short.

So why is public key cryptography such a big deal – 'revolutionary' as I described it earlier?

First of all, it is actually shocking to the point of being almost unbelievable that you can tell the whole world your enciphering key *without* this information revealing anything about your deciphering key. A public key system is based on publishing, for the whole world to see – legitimate users and others – the means by which messages are enciphered in the full confidence that this knowledge alone does not lead to the deciphering processes being discovered in a realistic amount of time. Before the advent of public key cryptography, cryptographic systems (which are now called 'private key' or 'classical' systems) depended for their security on both keys being kept private. With such systems, should one or other of the keys become known, then it is computationally feasible to obtain the other one. (In the Caesar system, knowing the decryption key reveals the encryption key immediately.)

What is revolutionary as well as enormously practical about public key cryptography is that it saves an awful lot of hassle! Why? Because it provides a solution to what is known as the problem of *key distribution*. Since it is necessary to keep both keys in a classical system private, Alice and Bob must first of all meet in secret if they want to fix on a classical system and on the keys to be used. (If they don't wish to do this, they must get a trusted courier to act as a go-between.) This is not always convenient, particularly if one lives in Dublin and the other in Berlin. They cannot trust email or any other insecure form of communication. Now take a million (which is not a lot in the modern world of business) such Alices and Bobs, all wishing to talk to each other in private. How many such meetings must there be? (For ten people, 45 such meetings are needed. Why?) Answer: about 500000000000, or half a million million. That's a lot of secret meetings, necessitating a lot of travel and time.

In Code

There is no need for any of this globetrotting with public key cryptography. Just look up the public directory to get the other person's enciphering transformation, and write to them in private to introduce yourself.

Another revolutionary aspect of certain public key systems is the really smart way they solve the problem of *message authentication* while achieving a little more besides.

A Signature Scheme

Bob, who is a technologically very up-to-date bank official in Very-Rich Bank, received the following ciphertext:

**$3iu%1bdfe&nKr7qn\$khg&*)vd\$1\}rAbz9hcq21bv%8&£22'/Bd15
sdvso£*sa6ph&gpsenbu*&%ks\$8g%g8s\$!kb8kkYTu11arq8(yt
ifan£19dr5 h\$ghkt6nvt&93sjlH**

on his computer terminal on 12 December 1999.

When he applied his private deciphering transformation f_B^{-1} to the ciphertext, he obtained the following interesting message:

> Dear Bob,
> Would you please transfer one thousand
> pounds from my account to my sister
> Joan's. I wish to give her a surprise
> Christmas present.
>
> Happy Christmas!
>
> Alice

How can Bob be sure that it really was Alice who sent this very nice message?

Since anyone wishing to impersonate Alice can look up Bob's enciphering transformation f_B in the public key directory, might it

One Way Only

not be the case (perish the thought!) that Joan actually sent this message that purports to come from her generous sister Alice? How can a message such as this be authenticated?

If the public one-way trapdoor function f has the additional property that

$$f[f^{-1}(P)] = P$$

then Alice can append a signature S to her message which allows Bob to authenticate it.

Before describing how, note that the property just described means that the deciphering transformation is first applied to a piece of plaintext (to give gobbledygook, as it will) and then the enciphering transformation is applied to recover the original plaintext. This is the opposite of what normally goes on in the enciphering/deciphering process. (In the Caesar system it would mean moving back three characters first and then forward three.)

Alice does the following:

1. She composes a 'signature', S. (I'm being deliberately vague about its nature.)
2. Alice then applies her deciphering transformation f_A^{-1} to the signature S (she is the only one who knows this function f_A^{-1}) and appends the result, $f_A^{-1}(S)$, to the end of her message. (Often it is this $f_A^{-1}(S)$ that is thought of as the signature.)
3. She then enciphers both her message and her 'decrypted' signature, f_A^{-1}, using Bob's enciphering transformation f_B, and sends the encrypted document to Bob.
4. Bob deciphers the incoming ciphertext to learn that the message purports to come from Alice. When he applies f_B^{-1} to the signature portion $f_B[f_A^{-1}(S)]$ to get $f_A^{-1}(S)$, it appears as gobbledygook. He now looks up Alice's enciphering transformation f_A in the public directory and applies it to $f_A^{-1}(S)$ to get

$$f_A[f_A^{-1}(S)] = S$$

In Code

In this way the signature is recovered and the message is authenticated.

Is this good enough? It is on the face of it, because there seems to be no doubt that S could have come from anyone other than Alice. Nobody, but nobody, except Alice, knows f_A^{-1}.

What if Alice is careless and Bob is a baddie? Suppose that Alice's signature consisted of the single word 'Alice'. What could Bad Bob do? Almost anything, because he could cut and paste this decrypted signature onto other messages written by himself but purporting to come from Alice. If he were cheeky and crazy enough he might even instruct his own bank to transfer funds from Alice's account to his. Should there be any raised eyebrows at all the money now on its way to his account, he can no doubt point to a gushing letter extolling his virtues as the friendliest bank teller alive, and if this glowing account does not dispel all doubts about the transaction then he need only point to the signature, which could only have come from Alice.

So, ingenious as this signature scheme is, it needs a little fine tuning to be used properly. This is achieved by making the signature S, in addition to being *signer*-dependent, *message*-dependent. Otherwise the message could be modified. Had Alice composed a signature S along the lines

Re transfer of £1000 to Joan's a/c, Alice, 10.00 a.m., 12/12/99

containing as it does her name, a brief résumé of the message, and the time and date, then Bad Bob can do nothing.

The signature scheme described does a little more than allow a message to be authenticated. It also has the feature that the message cannot be repudiated. Should Alice have a change of heart at a later time, she cannot deny having sent this message since nobody but she knows f_A^{-1}.

What could Alice do if in the above signature she failed to specify the exact amount of money, and Bad Bob worked his charms on Joan to collude with him in increasing the amount by a factor of ten or even a hundred? You can never be too careful!

One Way Only

The RSA Public Key Cryptosystem

Although Diffie and Hellman introduced the concept of one-way trapdoor functions and explained to the world the radical consequences of their existence, it was Ronald Rivest, Adi Shamir and Leonard Adleman of MIT who, in 1977, first exhibited an example of one which is fairly simple and lends itself to easy implementation. No one has ever proved a purported one-way function to be one, but the three inventors of what is now known as the RSA cryptosystem had very strong empirical evidence that the function they employed is indeed one-way in character. The scheme they developed is based in part on the belief that it is tremendously difficult to factorise 'large' composite integers, a belief backed by centuries of failed attempts to find one single efficient method.

I shall describe this celebrated system, which has withstood all forms of attack since it first saw the light of day in the August 1977 issue of *Scientific American*. Although it is unavoidably technical, it is relatively simple to describe, and anyone who has followed the mathematical exposition this far, even superficially, will be able to appreciate the general character of the scheme and see most of the mathematical ideas coming into play. Just read on and don't worry. You'll be surprised and rewarded by obtaining some notion of what is involved.

S t a r t - u p : This need be done only once.

1. Generate, at random, two prime numbers p and q of 100 digits or more.
2. Calculate $n = p \times q$ and $\phi(n) = n - (p + q) + 1$.
3. Generate, at random, a number $e < \phi(n)$ such that e is relatively prime to $\phi(n)$.
4. Calculate the multiplicative inverse, d, of e modulo $\phi(n)$, using the Euclidean algorithm.

P u b l i s h : Make public the enciphering key,

In Code

$$K_E = \langle n, e \rangle$$

Keep Secret: Conceal the deciphering key,

$$K_D = \langle n, d \rangle$$

Enciphering: The enciphering transformation is

$$C = f(P) = P^e \bmod n$$

Deciphering: The deciphering transformation is

$$P = f^{-1}(C) = C^d \bmod n$$

That's all there is to it!

"OK, but what is it all about, and what does $\phi(n)$ mean?"

I'll say something about $\phi(n)$ a little later (it is also discussed in Appendix D). There is no need to get distracted by it. Just think of it as a (certain important) number.

Suppose the public key $K_E = \langle n, e \rangle$ published above belongs to Bob. Such a key might look like

3158047947602683834343402871132072584715488222894775015428152222808368344736897467605980757546290594836395556373144745242759035196176119637870933244742660580931814608712962665610564695478209228003844429

56373143474524275903751961761143434028711320725847154882742660580931814608712980479476026268974676059833244174215121212181018138146087129632646759681203516048669352417584280797272

– two numbers which are pretty awesome in size; the first is Bob's *public modulus n* and the second is his *public encryption exponent e*. These are all I need to know to be able to send a message to Bob in encrypted form.

One Way Only

When I have written my message I divide it into blocks, called 'message units', and assign each a number P (the numerical equivalent of the message unit). I must choose the block size so that no P ever exceeds n, but this is easy to do. Now I encipher each P by calculating

$$C = P^e \bmod n$$

in turn to get a stream of C-numbers (the corresponding ciphertext numerical equivalents). *This is where I am making use of Bob's public encryption key*, $K_E = \langle n, e \rangle$. Of course, I have a program (written or purchased) which does all I have just described automatically in a matter of seconds.

This done, I press the 'Send' button, and a file with a seemingly meaningless mess of gigantic numbers makes its way to Bob's computer. When Bob receives this file of C-numbers he takes each in turn and calculates $C^d \bmod n$. *This is where Bob makes use of his private or secret decryption key*, $K_D = \langle n, d \rangle$. (It is only the d-number which is secret, as n is known.) Amazingly, he gets back the original set of P-numbers, which he then converts to plaintext so as to read my message. Of course, like me he has a program which carries out all these steps automatically. In fact the program is pretty much the same as the one I use because the encryption and decryption procedures in the RSA are exactly the same in character – I calculate $P^e \bmod n$, while Bob must calculate $C^d \bmod n$.

It is fascinating that in order to recover the P-numbers that I disguised as C-numbers by raising them to the power e, Bob actually re-raises! Rather than extracting eth roots by some complicated algorithm, he succeeds in undoing the first power raising by raising the C-numbers to the power d.

This 'poker tactic', as Dad calls it, works because e and d have been chosen very cleverly and it is the Euler–Fermat theorem of 1736 – or, if you want to stretch a point, Fermat's Little Theorem of 1640 – which explains how and why it works. I'll spare you the details (which are not that difficult) and say only that these number-theory results are pivotal in establishing the soundness of the RSA encryption/decryption procedure.

"But doesn't the enciphering/deciphering procedure take an eternity, considering the enormity of the numbers involved. Any P or C can be hundreds of digits in length, and these numbers must be raised to the exponents e and d respectively, each of which also can be hundreds of digits in length."

"Yes."

"Well, won't the resulting numbers go through the roof?"

"No."

"Why not?"

"Because all the arithmetic is done with respect to the modulus n, which means that all calculations are done on numbers which never exceed n."

"I suppose that is something, but it must still take quite some time since n is still an enormous number."

"Computing $P^e \bmod n$ using the fast exponentiation algorithm requires about 600 calculations when e is a 100-digit number. More efficient procedures are known."

"Hmm."

The *exponentiation* steps, i.e. the calculation of $P^e \bmod n$ or $C^d \bmod n$ in the RSA are what make it, unfortunately, slower than classical cryptosystems. For this reason it is normally used on a one-off basis to decide on a classical system. The RSA algorithm works fine on short files, so it is ideal for deciding on – and exchanging – the keys of a classical system, which can then be used in all subsequent communications. At the moment, public key algorithms are about 1500 times slower than the classical ones available. But who knows? Somebody might come up with a system which will give the classical systems a run for their money. There is no suggestion that classical systems are less secure than public key systems, but the latter have some very attractive features. We live in hope.

Any More Questions?

There are millions of questions which can be asked in connection

One Way Only

with the RSA. Some are

1. Does it work?
2. Is it fast?
3. Is it secure?
4. What is the one-way trapdoor function?
5. Where is the trapdoor?
6. What is the current state of factorising?
7. Does the start-up procedure take long?
8. Are there enough primes?
9. Might two users pick the same two primes?

Let's take these questions in turn. As I've already said, it does work even if it is not as fast as one might like it to be. Is it secure? R, S and A in their original paper remarked that "since no techniques exist to *prove* that an encryption scheme is secure, the only test available is to see whether anyone can think of a way to break it". Well, since 1977 some of the world's finest mathematicians (who could call on any amount of computing power) have failed to find an attack which proves fatal to the RSA system. As its originators said in the same paper, "once the method has withstood all attacks for a sufficient length of time it may be used with a reasonable amount of confidence". That time is considered to have come, since the RSA is now accepted as a world-wide standard.

The one-way trapdoor function in the RSA is $f(x) = x^e \bmod n$. Apparently no one knows an efficient way of inverting this function without being able to factorise the modulus n. Since knowing the number d allows the function to be inverted with ease, d is regarded as the trapdoor.

The status of factorisation in 1997 can be seen from the following table, which gives the estimated time it would take to factorise a number of so many decimal digits using the best known algorithms available at the time (based on the assumption that the most basic operation takes a millionth of a second):

In Code

Number of decimal digits	Time (years)
150	<200
230	100000
300	3×10^7
400	3×10^9

To help put the last two of these figures in perspective, the age of our planet is about 5×10^9 years.

"You promised you'd explain what $\phi(n)$ means."

"I did. It stands for the number of numbers less than n which are relatively prime to it."

"So $\phi(26) = 12$ because, as you told us some time ago, the numbers less than 26 which have no factor other than 1 in common with it are the twelve numbers 1, 3, 5, 7, 9, 11, 15, 17, 19, 21, 23 and 25."

"Exactly. It is very easy to say what value $\phi(n)$ has when n is a prime p."

"Let me think. All the numbers less than p have no factor other than 1 in common with it because the only factors of a prime p are 1 and p."

"Yes."

"So, $\phi(p) = p - 1$ since $p - 1$ is the number of numbers less than p."

"Top class!"

"Is it difficult to explain why $\phi(n) = n - (p + q) + 1$, as stated in the start-up procedure?"

"Not really, but are you sure you want me to?"

"Why not? It can't be that hard, the answer looks simple enough. You just subtract p and q from n and add back 1."

"Right. The only numbers which have a non-trivial factor in common with $n = p \times q$ are either multiples of p or of q, since p and q are primes. If $p = 5$ and $q = 7$, so that $n = p \times q = 5 \times 7 = 35$, then the multiples of 5, namely 5, 10, 15, 20, 25, 30 and 35, along with the multiples of 7, which are 7, 14, 21, 28 and 35, are the only numbers with a non-trivial factor in common with 35."

"I'm with you so far."

One Way Only

"Now, notice that the set of multiples of p contains q numbers, while the set of multiples of q contains p numbers. Check the example to see."

"OK. There are 7 multiples of 5 and 5 multiples of 7. Great!"

"Now, these two sets of multiples have no element in common, other ..."

"... than $p \times q$, so there are $(p + q) - 1$ numbers with a non-trivial factor in common with n."

"Yes."

"I've got it now. There are $n - [(p + q) - 1] = n - (p + q) + 1$ numbers relatively prime to n. That's why $\phi(n) = n - (p + q) + 1$. I'm a genius!"

"I've never doubted it."

"Can we go back to the RSA?"

"By all means."

"Might you not be able to get at d by searching?"

"It is possible – but not feasible – if Bob goes about his business properly."

" All right, then, calculate $\phi(n)$ and you're within reach of d, because Bob has revealed its inverse, e. Since d is the inverse of e, just calculate e's inverse to get d."

"Absolutely spot on, but how did you calculate $\phi(n)$?"

"Hmm, let me see. Well, I know n, so couldn't I just calculate all the numbers relatively prime to n?"

"And how would you do that?"

"Oh! I'd have to test every number less than n with Euclid's algorithm. That's out of the question because n is so big. If this approach made it possible to do the calculation quickly, I'd actually end up factorising n."

"Correct."

"Is there some other way of finding $\phi(n)$ without knowing the p and the q which are the factors of n?"

"Nobody has found a way, and if they did it would lead to a factorisation of n straight away."

"Interesting. I'll think about this, but of course it does mean that finding $\phi(n)$ must be as hard as the factorising problem."

In Code

"Yes. It is of paramount importance that $\phi(n)$ cannot be calculated, for a large $n = p \times q$, without knowledge of p and q."

"So, you've got to know your p's and q's."

"Apparently."

Does the start-up procedure take long? No. Once the primes p and q are generated, it is only a matter of microseconds to compute n and $\phi(n)$, and a matter of seconds to determine e and its multiplicative inverse, d, modulo $\phi(n)$ using the Euclidean algorithm. The fascinating part, which we have already discussed in connection with Fermat's Little Theorem, is that one can find 100-digit primes in a matter of minutes. Furthermore, there is absolutely no shortage of primes of this length because the prime number theorem can be used to show that there are approximately 4×10^{97} of them. One procedure uses a device which generates 100-digit numbers (of which there are exactly 9×10^{99}) at *random*; each subsequent odd number is then tested for primality until one which is prime is found. If you generate two primes in this way, the chances that someone else has one or other of them as part of their public modulus is less than my chances of winning the National Lottery ten weeks in a row.

One final point on the RSA system: its one-way trapdoor function has that all-important property necessary for a signature scheme. If a signature S is first raised to the power d modulo n and the result raised to the power e modulo n, then the original S reappears.

Official Secrets Out

In Simon Singh's *The Code Book* there is a section headed 'The Alternative History of Public-Key Cryptography' which tells a story I find a little sad. An Englishman named James Ellis, working for the Communications-Electronics Security Group (CESG) at the Government Communications Headquarters (GCHQ) in Cheltenham, came up with the concepts of public key cryptography before 1970. Thus, he anticipated Diffie and Hellman by about six years, but the world was not to know of his ideas at the time because he was sworn to secrecy. As Ellis himself relates, he was inispired by a Second World War Bell Telephone report by an unknown author which described an ingenious idea for secure telephone speech. Ellis referred to his form of cryptography as "non-secret encryption" and, like Diffie and Hellman, he had no definite scheme worked out which would actually implement the ideas.

About six weeks after joining the CESG in September 1973, a number-theorist by the name of Clifford Cocks was told of Ellis's ideas. While pondering them later that same day, he discovered in the space of half an hour what is now known as the RSA algorithm. Early the following year, an old school friend of Cocks, Malcolm Williamson, joined GCHQ as a cryptographer. When Cocks described his scheme to Williamson, the latter studied it carefully for many hours, certain that he would find a flaw somewhere in the reasoning. He couldn't. Instead, he discovered another crypto-graphic protocol, now termed the Diffie–Hellman–Merkle key exchange.

These three men have not yet become as famous as their American counterparts. Whether they do or not seems to be a matter of indifference to them, which is something I find truly admirable. I wonder who was the unknown author of that Bell Telephone report.

Some other cryptographic matters

Before we left the subject of cryptography, Dad talked a little about other odds and ends which he thought we might find of some interest. First he told a story about a young girl solving a certain problem in the company of older, more knowledgeable people which he said should encourage anyone just to think. Do not be intimidated, and do not adopt negative or unjustified attitudes such as, "How could I possibly solve this when I know so little about the topic?" Be more upbeat and think along the lines, "This sounds interesting, it can't be all that difficult, I wonder how this might be

In Code

done?" Sometimes you are better off not knowing whether a problem is (supposed to be) difficult or not, like the student who, arriving in a lecture hall shortly after a lecture had ended, took down the two problems remaining on the blackboard. Later he handed in their solutions, not knowing that the problems were not meant as homework but were examples of unsolved (up to then) problems. Does this true story remind you of a certain film?

Average Wage

Some years ago at a party, a group of mathematicians were asked, "How might you determine the average earnings of a group of people in a room (at a class reunion, perhaps) without any individual's divulging his or her salary?" While the grey-hairs went into over-drive pondering this, the young daughter of one of them piped up (don't read any further until you try for yourself), "I know how. Let me whisper a big number to the first person, and then let him add his salary to this number and write the answer on a piece of paper and pass it to the next person. This second person should add his salary to this new number and write his result on a *different* piece of paper, which he should pass to the third person. He must keep hidden the piece of paper he was given. Continue doing this all the way round the room until you reach the last person. Make sure that each person writes the answer on a piece of paper different from the one handed to him or her. When it gets to the last person I'll take the result and subtract my original big number to get the total of all their earnings. Then I can get the average."

This clever idea is known as a *zero-knowledge protocol* because it reveals no knowledge about any individual's salary.

How to Share a Secret

We are often asked "Can you keep a secret?" But how do you share a secret? And why might you want to do such a thing?

One Way Only

Alice, Bob and their friend Clare are working on a wonderful project and things are going really well. They are making great discoveries and are being as good as gold keeping detailed records of all their findings, though this is especially hard to do when they are just bursting to get on with experimenting to find out more exciting facts. All their important documents are kept, along with whatever else is vital to their work, safely locked in a cabinet out of harm's way. They are very fired up and would work night and day if it were physically possible. Up to now they have been very fortunate to be able to work as a complete team at times which have suited all three of them. Now, however, because of circumstances beyond their control, this will no longer be always possible. As it happens, some two of them, though not always the same two, could still meet. They agree for the sake of the project that at any one of these times the two people available should continue with the work and that the absent partner be briefed at the next meeting. However, they insist that no one of them should ever work alone, and though they are friends and trust one another, they agree to put themselves beyond temptation by locking the cabinet so that *any two* of them can open it but *no one* of them ever can. So how do they do this?

This is worth thinking about. Maybe I should tell you that they use more than one lock on the cabinet and distribute keys to these locks among themselves in a clever fashion. It is quite easy. When you come up with a method for doing this you will have implemented what is known as a *(2, 3)-threshold scheme*. Read no further until you have tried.

Here is what they do. They lock the cabinet using *three* locks, to each of which there are only two keys. If the locks are labelled L_1, L_2 and L_3 then Alice keeps a key to L_1 and L_2 (but not to L_3), Bob keeps a key to L_2 and L_3 (but not to L_1) while Clare keeps a key to L_1 and L_3 (but not to L_2). All six keys are used, and each person has two keys. Since each of them is missing a key to one lock, no one can ever open all three locks on his or her own. But any two have, between them, a full set of keys to all three locks, and so can open the cabinet.

You might like to help Alice, Bob and Clare to figure out what

163

to do if they wish Denis to join their team and still maintain a threshold of two, meaning that any two of the team of four can work without the others being present. In other words, they need you to help them come up with a (2, 4) scheme. Will they have to buy more locks, or can they get away with making more keys to the locks they already have? It is not so obvious how to implement this scheme with locks and keys.

What if we increase the number of people to 11 say, and the threshold to 6?

A (6, 11) scheme: *Eleven scientists are working on a secret project. They wish to lock documents in a cabinet such that the cabinet can be opened if and only if six or more of the scientists are present. What is the smallest number of locks needed? What is the smallest number of keys to the locks each scientist must carry?*

Now things get a little bizarre. This delightful problem is cited at the beginning of a paper by Adi Shamir, the S in the RSA, with the title 'How to Share a Secret'. It was in this short paper that Dad first learned about threshold schemes and their uses. He read it to us in sections, saying when he was finished, "Now that is how a paper should be written".

The surprise is that, without having to know how to go about it, or in fact knowing whether it is possible, it can be argued that *at least* 462 locks are needed with each scientist carrying *at least* 252 keys.

Can you imagine this, just for eleven scientists? Apart from the fact that they couldn't carry all these keys around on their persons, they would spend all day opening (and shutting) the cabinet, which would look like nothing on earth with 462 locks attached to it. So much for this mechanical solution!

Having beautifully illustrated the impracticality of implementing such a cumbersome scheme, the paper proceeds in a clear and direct way to promise an alternative clean electronic solution based on relatively simple mathematics. Rather than use locks and keys, the idea is to share some secret number D, such as a safe

One Way Only

combination or cryptographic key, by breaking it up into several 'pieces'. These pieces (called 'shadows') are other numbers related to D which on their own reveal nothing about it. Each member of the group is given a piece. In order to recover D, a certain minimum number (the threshold) of people from the group must combine their pieces in a certain way. Any number of people below this threshold cannot find D using their pieces: it lies beyond reach.

The digital signing of cheques is one application of such a threshold scheme. The idea is simple. Suppose you are the president of a company but cannot always be available to sign some of the important cheques that must be issued from time to time. What do you do? Give one or all of the five vice-presidents the power of signature? No, you are not that trusting. You arrange matters so that a cheque is considered signed only if it has a certain number or digital signature D printed on it electronically by a special device. You use a $(3, 5)$ scheme to create five shadows of D and have them printed on magnetic cards, and you give each of the five VPs a different card. When any three of these are read by the device it temporarily reconstructs D using the simple but clever mathematics behind the scheme, and signs the cheque digitally. Once this is done, the device destroys all traces of the number D and the numbers read from the cards. Two VPs cannot collude to defraud the company, for their two pieces alone are not enough to generate D. So this scheme affords a certain measure of safety. It is also very flexible. If you promote a new person to VP, she too can be given a new shadow by simply extending to a $(3, 6)$ scheme. If you trust one VP, say your daughter, more than the others, or want to give her more authority over the signing of cheques, then you might give her a second shadow.

At this point I have said just about everything I wished to say about cryptography, and of course a whole lot more than was absolutely necessary. In the next chapter I talk a little about the extra mathematics I had to learn when I began to investigate a new public key system. Even if you have acquired only the barest understanding of the central notions and terminology of cryptography, you'll have no trouble following the rest of the story. From here on it's mainly non-mathematical in nature.

6. Exhibition Time

As the time for Esat Young Scientist '98 drew near, Dad thought that I should have a few practice runs at explaining my project. It would help me to get my ideas clear, and was bound to improve my verbal presentation. The project contained many ideas which would need to be made simple and interesting. I would stand at the small blackboard in our kitchen and begin talking, and every so often Dad asked me a question as Mom listened. She would say afterwards at which points she felt I didn't explain something well enough or I went too fast. I knew this was a good idea because I had no experience of public speaking of any kind, but I hated these sessions with a vengeance. They made me feel so self-conscious. I did three or four of these mock presentations and each time the hardest hurdle was to begin speaking. I suppose it was because it all seemed so fake, but these sessions were very helpful and made me feel better prepared.

What I much preferred was going for half-hour walks with Dad along the quiet country roads near our house. Here I could talk without being looked at or having to look at anyone. I could concentrate much better this way. Mostly I talked and Dad just listened. I wanted to get the sequence of ideas ordered correctly, to sense their general outline and to distinguish what was important from what was more technical detail. All this helped me to prepare a verbal presentation of about fifteen minutes in length. That is roughly the amount of time allotted to a contestant to describe his or her project to a judge. It would be terrible to run out of time without having got to the really interesting stuff. The more I explained the ideas, the more I could see what questions people might ask. So I thought a little more and understood more. Dad would also ask the odd question. "Better I ask you questions tougher than anyone else will." These walks were very pleasant and got me out into the fresh winter air doing something healthy.

The hardest part of the project was writing it up. It is such a long and tiring process because by now I was almost as much a perfectionist as my father. It was an exacting ordeal, and other things which should have been done much sooner were left literally to the last minute. The night before I was due in Dublin I just about finished putting together my poster presentation for the project and editing the slides I had prepared with the Microsoft package PowerPoint. The following morning I was up at six o'clock to catch an early train. At the time it was both disconcerting and exciting that I had no idea of my project's standard or how it might compare with that of other entrants. I was afraid that some of the other projects might make mine seem trivial, which is something I wouldn't have liked. However, no matter how different my project might be, or whatever its standard, I was certainly going to learn a lot by attending the exhibition. Although I didn't know what to expect I did feel that I had done a lot of work, and I was pleased with the clear, simple written report which I eventually put together for presentation to the judges.

Never having even visited the exhibition before, my first reaction was one of total 'gobsmackification'. It was so colourful and noisy and there were so many displays. I felt like a child at a fairground. There were over six hundred projects in all, entered in three categories – Biological and Ecological Sciences, Behavioural Sciences, and Physics, Chemistry and Mathematics. My project was an individual entry (as opposed to a team or group entry) in the last of these categories. Of the three age categories, Junior, Intermediate and Senior, I was in the Intermediate category. Before setting up my own display I had a look at some of the other exhibits. Those in the senior section seemed to me unfathomable, but over the following days I learned a little about them and became more relaxed. I never fooled myself into thinking that I had a chance of winning one of the two main prizes for individuals, but instead set my sights on a category award. The other contestants from my school did not seem to be as anxious as I was. Vincent was an old pro – this was his third time of entering. He tried to get me to relax while I was waiting for the judges, but I just couldn't. What would the judges be like? Would I have to do all the talking, or would they ask lots of questions? What kinds of question might they ask? Would they be interested at all?

There were three judging periods, one on the first afternoon and two more in the morning and afternoon of the next day. None of the interviews with my three judges was the same. Each was new and scary, interesting and worthwhile. I felt I fared better in the second and third sessions than I did in the first. I was happy with the length of time that each judge spent with me and the interest each showed in the subject of the project. The whole experience, from the preparation of my report, display and presentation, right down to meeting the other competitors and hearing about the other projects, is something I would never have missed. I'd encourage anyone who is interested in any of the sciences to participate in science contests, not for the prizes but for the excitement of working on something of your own choice and the atmosphere at the fairs. For me, the judges' interviews were the best experience – educational and motivating. It is rewarding to see all your hard work paying off when a judging session goes well or people compliment you on your display. Getting constructive criticism from one of my judges at Young Scientist '98 was the main reason I entered the competition again in '99. Also, I felt from listening to others' experiences with the judges and from seeing their displays that I could do a little better the next time round by applying what I had learned. I just knew I had gained experience.

The contest was won by Raphael Hurley, another Cork entrant, whose project display was on a stand next to mine. He's a son of a friend of my father's and I grew quite friendly with him during the week. He had carried out a mathematical analysis of the game of Monopoly with the help of *Mathematica*, so our projects had something in common. I too was to be delighted with my result. During the main award ceremony on the third evening of the exhibition, Friday, I was so happy when my name was announced as the winner of the Individual Intermediate Mathematics, Physics and Chemistry category. The next day, special awards were given out, and my late nights before the exhibition spent cutting and sticking cardboard were shown to have paid off when I won the Display Award for the same section. But it was at a small ceremony just before the closing of the exhibition on Sunday that I was to receive my biggest prize. I was not even aware this prize existed, so I was taken completely by surprise when I was called up to accept the Intel Excellence Award. The recipient of this award would represent Ireland at the Intel International Science and Engineering Fair (ISEF) to be held at Fort Worth, Texas, later in the year. I could not believe it. This was a huge prize and I was totally shocked. While everyone else was packing up their exhibits just minutes after this ceremony, I had to let Dad take care of mine. I was walking around in a daze.

Days later, as I started to drop down a few clouds, I began to think of how I could improve my project for the ISEF. Foremost in my mind was the thought that I would have to do something extra to bring it up to what I imagined would be 'international standard', though I knew I was quite entitled to take it to Texas as it stood. However, I felt it lacked a certain amount of originality, so I was keen to find some way of strengthening it. After one science exhibition I felt more confident and wanted to do my best. I discovered what kind of a challenge lay ahead of me when I read with awe descriptions of some of the projects which had been past winners. I knew I had a lot of work to do. While it was not necessary to expand my project for the competition, it was an absolute must for me. From that week on I was on the look-out for new ideas.

One consequence of my having won the Intel Award was an invitation to give a short talk on cryptography to my fellow classmates in the Enrichment Course in Mathematics. This is a special course given on Saturday mornings during term by some dedicated lecturers at University College Cork for school students with a particular interest in mathematics. Some of the older students in the class had been selected as possible members of the Irish Maths Olympiad Team, so I knew I would be talking to some smart cookies. If this wasn't daunting enough, my knowing a few of them fairly well made the prospect of talking in front of them an even worse prospect. Having given a number of talks since that time, I know now that I always feel much happier speaking to a group of complete strangers, preferably ones I shall never meet again. It was the first time I had ever been a guest speaker and it taught me a lot, mainly that I hate addressing groups of people.

Dad often says "the right thing is always the hard thing". When it comes to making tough decisions I've found this to be very true. I remind myself of this advice whenever I'm tempted to take the easy way out. One hard decision which I am now glad I made was about my choice of work experience during my Transition year. This programme is designed to give students an opportunity to work for a week or two in a company or an industry which they might like to join after finishing school or college. Many use it to get a foot in the door of a local business so they can get a summer job there later in the year. I wanted, however, to make the most of this opportunity in a way which would benefit me much further into the future.

I decided to be adventurous and search the Internet to see if there were any cryptography companies in Ireland. I found the names of three, and after doing a little further digging I emailed my CV to the one I had picked as my first choice, Baltimore Technologies. Needless to say I took care to mention that I'd received my Intel Award for a project on cryptography. I remember the feeling of excitement as I wrote that letter. When a reply came with an invitation to spend a week with these information security specialists, I could not have been more pleased and frightened at the same time. But I was determined not to let an opportunity like this pass me by, and though I feared I might find myself way out of my depth in the company of top cryptographers, I made myself go. At the time I had had little exposure to what working in a computer company might be like, and I knew very little about what it is people do in most technical areas. It was not normal for students from our school to go beyond Cork in search of a work-experience placement, as Transition year co-ordinators must visit each student to make sure that everything is going well. Since Baltimore is a Dublin-based company it looked as if I would be spared this visit.

Whenever I look back at my time at Baltimore I get a renewed sense of the excitement I felt while I was there. Dr William Whyte, their senior cryptographer, took me under his wing immediately and treated me as an equal. He gave me truly challenging tasks and so spared me the fate of having to make tea and stuff envelopes. To top a very enjoyable but too short stay I got a magnificent reference from William, some of which I now quote as it describes the experience I gained better than I could.

> Given her background, when she arrived we wanted to give her a project that would challenge her and make proper use of her abilities. By its nature, this meant giving her work that was perhaps harder than she'd been expecting. I am pleased to say that she rose to the challenge magnificently. She worked independently on concepts that most students only encounter late in their undergraduate courses. She was perfectly happy to have the concepts explained to her and then work on her own to realise them. She took up our time only when it was necessary and asked focused, directed questions. It's been a pleasure to have her both as an office-mate and as a colleague, and we wish her all the best in the future.

I think this reference says as much about its author as it does about me. I was again to experience this same generosity of spirit a number of times from distinguished men and women. In Irish there is a saying, *Mol an óige agus tiocfaidh sí*, which roughly means, 'Praise youth and it will flourish'.

While at Baltimore, William gave me a draft of an unpublished paper by a colleague of his, Dr Michael Purser, the founder of the company, who at the time was away on a fishing holiday. The paper explored a possible new public key cryptographic scheme based on mathematics which was unknown to me. My task was to try to write code to see whether I could implement its ideas and get 'something working'. Before I could get down to programming I had to familiarise myself with the mathematics. Dad got one or two frantic emails asking for the most basic and, whenever possible, concise explanations of terms. I know I could have sought William's help, and on occasion I did, but I didn't want to bother him too much. It's OK to bother dads but not busy bosses.

As *Mathematica*'s was the only programming language I knew, William allowed me to use his ID to access the copy of the program on Trinity College's Web site. So I set to work. I read some of the paper, wrote a piece of code, read some more, wrote some more. Eventually the program began to take shape and the mathematical ideas lost some of their strangeness. By the end of my stay and after much effort I had a working implementation of the system. I had also become intrigued by the mathematical ideas which had occupied my thoughts for the last four days.

When I returned home I thought, "Wouldn't it be great if I could work on some of the ideas in Dr Purser's paper?" If I were to study and present a detailed discussion of them, it would really enhance my project and give it an original element. By 'original' I don't mean my own ideas, but something not to be found in the current science journals. However, even if Dr Purser would give me the go-ahead to use his ideas, it would still be better if I could add something new of my own. I remember talking to Dad about how the scheme described in his paper exploits a property known as non-commutative multiplication (meaning that $a \times b$ need not be the same as $b \times a$). Dad suggested that if I wanted a different setting in which to exploit this simple but very significant property I could use matrices, because matrix multiplication is also non-commutative. I was 'all ears', though I knew nothing about matrices. I'll share with you in a moment a little of what I had to learn about them so that I can give you a glimpse of what it means for matrix multiplication to be non-commutative. I promise that from then on there will be no more explicit mathematics, only light explanations of mathematical ideas.

I became all fired up and decided that I would just have to pluck up the courage to phone Dr Purser. Before the phone conversation

Exhibition Time

I was shaking with worry about how he would react to my request. After all, he is a highly respected mathematician educated at Trinity College, Dublin, and Cambridge, and I was just an upstart of a secondary school student having the nerve to phone him at his home seeking permission to use his ideas.

I introduced myself nervously, apologising for making so bold as to contact him. When I ran my request by him he answered, "Of course, fire ahead". I was so taken aback by this immediate reply (though it was the one I had wanted to hear) that I was lost for words. He was delighted that someone, particularly someone so young, would take an interest. I couldn't thank him enough. Hours later I was still thinking of the conversation I had just had and the fact that I could now work on something new and fresh. I guessed there would be an awful lot of work ahead of me, but I was very excited. I wrote a quick email to William telling him of my phone call. An almost instant reply wished me the best of luck. I did not meet or get to know Dr Purser until some time later. I now take the liberty of calling him Michael.

2×2 Matrices

Matrices are an invention of Sir Arthur Cayley, a brilliant English mathematician of the nineteenth century. The array of numbers

$$\begin{pmatrix} 5 & 6 \\ 12 & 2 \end{pmatrix}$$

is an example of a 2×2 (read as 'two by two') matrix. It is so called because it has two rows and two columns. It has four *entries* which, reading 'row-wise', are 5, 6, 12 and 2.

As with numbers, it is often convenient to refer to a matrix by a single letter, for example

$$\mathbf{A} = \begin{pmatrix} 5 & 6 \\ 12 & 2 \end{pmatrix}$$

In Code

Another example of a 2 × 2 matrix is

$$\mathbf{B} = \begin{pmatrix} 4 & 5 \\ 3 & 9 \end{pmatrix}$$

Two matrices are added by adding their corresponding entries. For example,

$$\begin{pmatrix} 5 & 6 \\ 12 & 2 \end{pmatrix} + \begin{pmatrix} 4 & 5 \\ 3 & 9 \end{pmatrix} = \begin{pmatrix} 5+4 & 6+5 \\ 12+3 & 2+9 \end{pmatrix}$$

It is natural to label this matrix sum as $\mathbf{A} + \mathbf{B}$. Thus,

$$\mathbf{A} + \mathbf{B} = \begin{pmatrix} 9 & 11 \\ 15 & 11 \end{pmatrix}$$

Check that the matrix $\mathbf{B} + \mathbf{A}$ is the same as $\mathbf{A} + \mathbf{B}$. In general,

$$\mathbf{A} + \mathbf{B} = \mathbf{B} + \mathbf{A}$$

Matrix addition shares this 'commutative property' with ordinary addition.

The rule for multiplying two 2 × 2 matrices is more complicated. Here is how the matrix $\mathbf{A}$ is multiplied by the matrix $\mathbf{B}$:

$$\begin{pmatrix} 5 & 6 \\ 12 & 2 \end{pmatrix} \times \begin{pmatrix} 4 & 5 \\ 3 & 9 \end{pmatrix} = \begin{pmatrix} 5 \times 4 + 6 \times 3 & 5 \times 5 + 6 \times 9 \\ 12 \times 4 + 2 \times 3 & 12 \times 5 + 2 \times 9 \end{pmatrix}$$

Using the natural notation $\mathbf{A} \times \mathbf{B}$ to denote the product of the matrix $\mathbf{A}$ by the matrix $\mathbf{B}$, this calculation shows that

$$\mathbf{A} \times \mathbf{B} = \begin{pmatrix} 38 & 79 \\ 54 & 78 \end{pmatrix}$$

This multiplication process may strike you as totally unintelligible. As a first step to explaining how the entries of the product $\mathbf{A} \times \mathbf{B}$

are calculated, we might say that each is obtained by multiplying the appropriate row of **A** by the appropriate column of **B**. For example, the entry, 54, of **A** × **B** which is in the second row and the first column, is obtained by multiplying the corresponding row of **A** by the corresponding column of **B**. Thus the second row of **A**, which is (12 2), is multiplied by the first column of **B**, which is

$$\begin{pmatrix} 4 \\ 3 \end{pmatrix}$$

This row is multiplied by this column in the following manner:

$$(12 \quad 2) \; \times \; \begin{pmatrix} 4 \\ 3 \end{pmatrix} \; = \; 12 \times 4 + 2 \times 3$$
$$= \; 48 + 6$$
$$= \; 54$$

What has been done here is that the corresponding entries of the row and column have been multiplied and their results added. Thus the first entry of the row, 12, multiplies the first entry of the column, 4, to give 48. The second entry of the row, 2, multiplies the second entry of the column, 3, to give 6. Their results 48 and 6 are then added to give 54.

To calculate the entry 79, which appears in the first row and the second column of **A** × **B** you multiply the first row of **A** by the second column of **B**. This is done exactly as described above. Here is the calculation:

$$(5 \quad 6) \; \times \; \begin{pmatrix} 5 \\ 9 \end{pmatrix} \; = \; 5 \times 5 + 6 \times 9$$
$$= \; 25 + 54$$
$$= \; 79$$

See if you have got the hang of matrix multiplication by calculating for yourself the entry in the second row and the second column of **A** × **B**. It doesn't matter if you don't succeed – all that is important is that you can get the gist of what follows.

Now, when the matrix **B** is multiplied by the matrix **A** we have

$$\begin{pmatrix} 4 & 5 \\ 3 & 9 \end{pmatrix} \times \begin{pmatrix} 5 & 6 \\ 12 & 2 \end{pmatrix} = \begin{pmatrix} 4 \times 5 + 5 \times 12 & 4 \times 6 + 5 \times 2 \\ 3 \times 5 + 9 \times 12 & 3 \times 6 + 9 \times 2 \end{pmatrix}$$

Again using the natural notation **B** × **A** to denote the multiplication of the matrix **B** by the matrix **A**, this calculation shows that

$$\mathbf{B} \times \mathbf{A} = \begin{pmatrix} 80 & 34 \\ 123 & 36 \end{pmatrix}$$

There is a surprise in store when we compare the two products **A** × **B** and **B** × **A** to see whether they are 'equal'. Two matrices are considered to be equal if, and only if, *all* their corresponding entries match (which seems a natural enough definition of equality for matrices). We find that

$$\mathbf{A} \times \mathbf{B} = \begin{pmatrix} 38 & 79 \\ 54 & 78 \end{pmatrix}$$

$$\mathbf{B} \times \mathbf{A} = \begin{pmatrix} 80 & 34 \\ 123 & 36 \end{pmatrix}$$

Compare the entries of **A** × **B** with the corresponding entries of **B** × **A** – they do not match.

So, in contrast to the ordinary multiplication of numbers, for which it is always true that $a \times b = b \times a$, it is usual, as in this case, for matrices **A** and **B** that

$$\mathbf{A} \times \mathbf{B} \neq \mathbf{B} \times \mathbf{A}$$

(the symbol ≠ means 'not equal to'). This is why matrix multiplication is said to be non-commutative.

Because matrix multiplication is non-commutative, things which are awkward in ordinary algebra become much more so in matrix algebra. For the ordinary numbers a and b,

$$(a + b)^3 = a^3 + 3a^2b + 3ab^2 + b^3$$

Here a^2b is being used instead of the longer $a^2 \times b$. The 'expansion' of $(a + b)^3$ on the right-hand side of this equation is unpleasant enough, but it is positively compact by comparison with its matrix counterpart:

$$(\mathbf{A} + \mathbf{B})^3 = \mathbf{A}^3 + 2\mathbf{A}^2\mathbf{B} + \mathbf{ABA} + 2\mathbf{AB}^2 + \mathbf{BAB} + \mathbf{B}^3$$

The expansion of $(a + b)^3$ is not as extended as this because the commutative property, $a \times b = b \times a$, for ordinary numbers allows compound terms like $a \times b + b \times a$ to be compressed into single ones like $2ab$. Unless $\mathbf{A} \times \mathbf{B} = \mathbf{B} \times \mathbf{A}$, a similar compression is not valid for the matrix expression $\mathbf{A} \times \mathbf{B} + \mathbf{B} \times \mathbf{A}$.

It is precisely because matrix multiplication is non-commutative that attempts are made to exploit this feature to design cryptosystems which are fast and secure. Of course, arithmetic is performed modulo some positive number, which has the effect of complicating matters even further. For example, working modulo 13,

$$\mathbf{A} \times \mathbf{B} = \begin{pmatrix} 5 & 6 \\ 12 & 2 \end{pmatrix} \times \begin{pmatrix} 4 & 5 \\ 3 & 9 \end{pmatrix} = \begin{pmatrix} 12 & 1 \\ 2 & 0 \end{pmatrix}$$

while

$$\mathbf{B} \times \mathbf{A} = \begin{pmatrix} 4 & 5 \\ 3 & 9 \end{pmatrix} \times \begin{pmatrix} 5 & 6 \\ 12 & 2 \end{pmatrix} = \begin{pmatrix} 2 & 8 \\ 6 & 10 \end{pmatrix}$$

Besides adding a little more mystery, working modulo some positive integer has the virtue of keeping the magnitude of the numbers being handled less than the size of the modulus.

When using matrices, plaintext is broken up into blocks which are assigned numerical equivalents in the usual way. These numbers are then taken four at a time and one each placed in the four positions of a 2×2 matrix. This 'plaintext matrix' is then transformed into a ciphertext matrix. The corresponding ciphertext is extracted by reversing the assignment procedures used in the encipherment.

The Intel International Science and Engineering Fair in Texas was coming up in May. One abiding memory I have of the last few days of March 1998 is of spending a vast amount of time laboriously filling out forms. After having completed what seemed like 201 of them, I had to write an abstract of the project I was submitting to the competition. This was pure torture, and was particularly difficult as I had nothing of any substance done on the 'new stuff'. I was still reading and learning the basics. In the end I wrote a synopsis of my Young Scientist '98 project and just added the following ambition:

> I am currently doing some extra work which I hope to use to broaden my project. I am investigating the possibility of constructing an asymmetric algorithm which exploits the non-commutative property of matrix multiplication.

Because I had chosen a different setting in which to apply Michael's ideas, I would be on my own when it came to proving that the proposed new system was as secure as the one I was intending to compare it with – the celebrated RSA, which was the showpiece of my Young Scientist '98 project and which is accepted as a worldwide standard. If (and it was a big if) I could get the theoretical end right, I was hoping to show that the new system had certain speed advantages over the RSA. The way I was going to do this was simply to implement both systems (I had the RSA already programmed) on a computer and compare their 'running times' – the times each would take to encipher and decipher an appreciable amount of text. I eventually ended up using twelve copies of the *Desiderata* (Go placidly ...) all strung together as my plaintext. This was going to be the easy but revealing part. Once I got the 'new' system programmed correctly it would simply be a matter of straightforward testing and recording, which I hoped would see it first past the post in the 'speed' race.

Exhibition Time

Why did the proposed new system (assuming it was as secure) hold out the prospect of being faster than the RSA? Because it uses only multiplication, while the established system (known to be secure) involves an exponentiation step, which is much slower. This was the hope. The new system's security was to hinge on the non-commutativity of multiplication and Michael's ingenious enciphering/deciphering scheme, and was faster than the RSA because it avoided that slow step fundamental to the older system's security.

So here I was in April, about a fortnight after my stint at Baltimore, counting on a chicken as yet to be hatched. By this time I had learned enough about matrices to have the new system up and running. The good news was that the speed trials showed this algorithm to be a clear winner. This was something at least, but it would be nothing if the system couldn't be shown to be secure against all conceivable attacks. This was where the real work would have to start. That is where the difference lay between what I had done for my first project and what I needed to do for the proposed extended project. All the mathematics for my first project is well known. I simply learned what was relevant to the material I presented and I wrote code to demonstrate some chosen crypto-systems in action. Now things were completely different. They were on a grander scale, and Michael's ideas were new, as was the proposed setting, so there was nothing to be found in textbooks relating directly to what I was hoping to undertake. The fact that I knew a certain amount of number theory and had assimilated some of the ideas of cryptography was obviously going to be a great help, but because I was no longer dealing simply with numbers but matrices I now needed to understand so much more mathematics. Normally one studies a topic in some depth before embarking on work which requires at least a basic knowledge of its content, but I didn't have the time. To prepare in a normal fashion might be to do part of a university course over a number of months. My hoping to achieve everything I knew I would have to in a very short period of time was like insisting on writing a book in an unfamiliar language using only a dictionary, rather than learning the language first.

In Code

Crazy, but what the heck?

To allay my fears and put me a bit at ease, Dad showed me a passage from E.T. Bell's *Men of Mathematics* which had struck him forcefully when he first read it as a young man. It tells of the great German mathematician Jacobi, warning about dilly-dallying and encouraging young people to be brave and just get 'stuck in' to whatever problem is at hand.

> Jacobi seems to have been the first regular mathematical instructor in a university to train students in research by lecturing on his own latest discoveries and letting the students see the creation of a new subject taking place before them. He believed in pitching young men into the icy water to learn to swim or drown by themselves. Many students put off attempting anything on their own account till they have mastered everything relating to their problem that has been done by others. The result is that but few ever acquire the knack of independent work. Jacobi combated this dilatory erudition. To drive home the point to a gifted but diffident young man who was always putting off doing anything until he had learned something more, Jacobi delivered himself of the following parable. 'Your father would never have married, and you wouldn't be here now, if he had insisted on knowing *all* the girls in the world before marrying *one*.'

Learning the basics about matrices wasn't as bad as I had imagined it might be in one of my many moments of panic. It was fun, and Dad mentioned a few applications of matrices, which had the effect of making them more real. The fact that I was going to be using them in a cryptographic system would be another application. I knew they had been used by Lester Hill in the 1930s in a classical cryptosystem. It was at this stage that I was able to program the new system and check the speed prediction experimentally. So the practical end was OK. I could try all sorts of variations and fine tunings whenever I just wanted to play.

But was the system secure? The only way to show this is to envisage all sorts of attacks and then show (hopefully) that none can succeed. Even at this point, it may be that some subtle or not so

1. Dad and I walking in the grounds of Blarney Castle on a cold afternoon in January.

2. Home with Blarney Castle in background on the left. Cork city lies beyond the hill which is in a line with our weather-beaten Scots pine and the gable end of the house.

3. Family in the conservatory, February 1999: Michael is between Mom and Dad with (l. to r.) Brian, Eamonn (in clownish humour) and David in front of me.

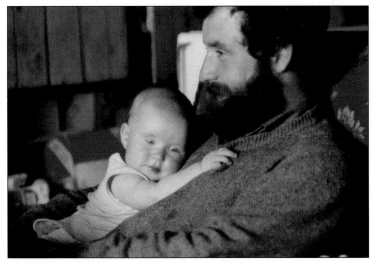

4. As a baby with Dad. I didn't grow any hair worth mentioning until I was two.

5. With Mom, February 1999. Why do I look so ??

6. With Baby Brian, Michael and Dad when I was five and a half, summer 1987.

7. Jumping 'Clydie' in Millstreet, Co. Cork, when I was 7
'Look up, Sarah, look up !' Sadly, my beloved Clydie had to be put down in 1999 when he should have been enjoying his retirement.

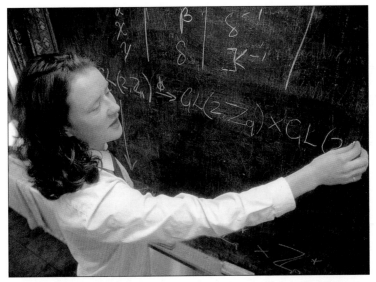

8. *At the blackboard sketching an outline of some of the ideas behind my cryptographic project.*

9. *Eamonn at the blackboard in the kitchen working on a puzzle watched by Dad and David. Mom standing behind me is the last, as usual, to sit down to her soup and rolls.*

10. *Discussing my project with Grandad at the Royal Dublin Society some hours after winning the 1999 Esat Telecom Young Scientist and Technology Exhibition.*

11. *Speaking with President Mary McAleese at Áras an Uachtaráin (the official residence of the President) on the Sunday after becoming Ireland's Young Scientist of the Year 1999.*

12. *In the computer room at school, Scoil Mhuire gan Smál, January 1999: I'm holding my Young Scientist trophy in the company (l. to r.) of the school principal, an t-Uasal Dónal O' Gárda, the Taoiseach, Bertie Ahern T.D., my classmate Vincent Foley (holding his Intel Excellence Award) and my science teacher, Seán Foley, Vincent's father.*

13. *Working on a laptop in Dad's study during the writing of this book. Everything on the bookshelves relates to Mathematics. The books on cryptography are on the shelf 'behind my nose'.*

14. Today.

subtle attack has been overlooked. Of course, you won't know this when you report on what was investigated and the conclusions that were reached. Another person might see a gaping hole in the system, but the hope is that this won't happen, and if it does, to try to deal with it. So in broad outline the plan was to attack and defend.

In order to answer the many questions which such investigations threw up, I had to ferret out as much relevant material as possible, which required 'going to the journals'; very specific subject matter is not to be found in general textbooks. This was a new experience and gave me a much better appreciation of the importance of good libraries. I remembered Dad saying that Gauss had chosen to attend Göttingen University rather than some other one because its library was better. I thought this a little odd at the time but I now understand it, even if it wouldn't be my overriding consideration in choosing a university. Initially with Dad's guidance, I spent hours in the libraries of the Cork Institute of Technology, where he works, and University College Cork, searching through the many mathematical journals and magazines for papers which might contain something that might shed some light. The papers which were to prove the most help to me came not from the 'very heavy' journals but from the lighter ones, whose articles contain plenty of mathematics but are written in an easy style aimed at keeping the reader's attention.

Then, of course, the papers had to be read very carefully. In the beginning Dad went through one or two of them with me, pointing out what I should be able to read, and what I couldn't be expected to understand, given my current state of knowledge. He knew I would get a terrible shock, so he warned me not to despair and advised that I read a paper through once quickly (even if most of it was double Dutch) to get a vague idea of whether it might be relevant. Even with this encouragement it was still a chilling experience at first, because I kept coming across terms I didn't recognise and results which were being taken for granted, but which I knew absolutely nothing about. This was a time of 'deep realisation'. If I ever had any doubts about how much work would have to be done, I certainly had none now.

It was easy to deal with new terms – look them up in a standard textbook or just ask Dad, but the results which were being quoted were an entirely different matter. "Dad, what is the Chinese Remainder Theorem?" might be answered by an explanation with a proof or one without, or it might simply be answered by "You can look it up in 'such and such' a book." One way or the other it normally meant at least a day's work just trying to figure it out. With a particularly interesting theorem, like the one just mentioned, I'd write a program to generate examples. I find this a great way (when possible) of getting to know a result. Whenever I programmed something I'd end up playing around for hours rather than getting back to plodding my way through the paper. Eventually back to the paper I would go, to decipher (!) a few more lines.

In time it became a little easier to recognise almost at a glance when a paper might be useful and, much later, even easier to read a paper right through while all the time on the look-out for material which would be 'bang on' for what I was doing. Those papers that held a promise of being helpful I read again and again.

All of this was an unusual experience for me, but I had a great feeling of excitement. I think it was because I was working on something that no one had worked on before. I worked constantly for whole days on end, and it was exhilarating. There were times when I never wanted to stop. Most of the time nothing was coming together and I was running into dead end after dead end. I kept different parts of the developing ideas on the blackboard in the kitchen, in particular those parts where I was stuck, so that they were there in front of me all the time waiting to be sorted out. Then there was the time when I came bounding down the stairs to tell Dad of a simple step which meant that all I had done before would fit together to finish a large part of a proof. It was a real joy when inspiration hit, but no time can be wasted with self-congratulatory back-slapping. It was a case of back to work on a full tank of enthusiasm.

As my understanding of mathematical ideas deepened, so too did my approach. I wanted to learn more and more and, thanks to

Exhibition Time

Dad, I wanted to learn it properly. I knew that it is reasonable to quote results and not be expected (probably) to be able to know how to prove them. Knowing them is often enough, but I started wanting to know how everything is proved. I wasn't happy to plough ahead and search for answers to other questions and assume that what I have read or been told is true (which it normally is) without getting sidetracked. When I did read a proof where the maths was far above my level of understanding I became frustrated and often wanted to learn the relevant maths, even though I knew it wasn't necessary and not directly related to what I was doing. I came to hate being told, "It's probably best understood by working through the proof, but it's too difficult." Everything Dad had taught me he taught me from the bottom up, beginning with "the fundamentals, Sarah, the fundamentals!"

Just to give a sample of the kind of things I was working on from day to day once things got under way, here are some extracts from my diary for that period, which I have come to regard as 'those extraordinary months'. (Don't worry about not knowing what is meant by each entry).

Started slowly – experimenting with matrices over finite fields and finite commutative rings – Made routine for generating random matrices – Learnt matrix algorithm 'Hill cipher' – Made own routine for finding inverses of matrices – Put together first enciphering and deciphering routine, only nine characters at a time though – Next step, get routine to work on lists of matrices – Wrote general routines after solving 'join problem' – Found **Flatten**[ ] command at 23:43 tonight (has solved loads of problems) – Investigated orders of groups – Surfed the net for papers and notes on various things including discrete logarithm problem – Ran first 'timing' using *Desiderata* $\times$ 12 – Investigated possible signature schemes, a big learning experience – Learned more about rings, groups etc. – Quadratic residues – Got two laptops from CIT which could talk to each other. (For display purposes) – M. Vandyck taught me about eigenvalues, eigenvectors etc. – M. Vandyck gave me an overview of spectral decomposition theory for extracting the roots of matrices –

In Code

Talked to Dr Pat Fitzpatrick, told him all the details, very helpful – Went to UCC and CIT libraries and looked at maths journals and number theory and linear algebra books – Found problem in routines (very silly mistake) – Programmed Hill cipher for interest – Solved lots of the problems in *Mathematica* stuff, put more restriction on different parts of the routines to stop any unforeseen problems with commutativity etc. – Got a fright in morning thinking that $\delta.\epsilon = \alpha.\delta$ would be solvable by linear equations but thankfully too many possible answers – A breakthrough. – Learnt Gaussian elimination from Dad – Got *Mathematica* to find all possible solutions for a few small examples – One-to-one mappings – Programmed row reduce. – Kept investigating how to find x and number of possible x's to fit certain equations – Went back to basics, testing myself, investigating groups of small order – Made a conjecture that the no. of invertible matrices in $GL(2, Z_n)$ = no. of invertible matrices in

$$GL(2, Z_p) \times GL(2, Z_q) = n\phi(n)^2(p + 1)(q + 1)$$

– how to prove with arguments like one for order of $GL(2, Z_p)$? Investigating $GL(2, Z_6)$ separating matrices of different determinants into groups – Investigating structure of subsets – Primitive elements – Listing 'pre-images' of quadratic residues – Wrote matrix routine to reduce modulo n at each step and tested this against the method I had been using for speed advantages – Reverted to old way after many tests – Testing against RSA – Plotted a few graphs of comparison times obtained empirically – Tidied up some files – Modified RSA routines to make p and $q \equiv 3 \bmod 4$ – Big change, changed routine to give a high-order element by making p and q both products of two times another prime plus 1 – Everything coming together – the end is in sight!

Speaking maths, writing maths, thinking maths nearly all the time was just so weird. I had a constant feeling of "I can't believe I'm working on this – I can't believe I'm working on maths like this!" I was enthralled by the work and found it fascinating. I came to understand Dad's obsession and could finally comprehend how a book – other than a school textbook – could be written on mathematics. When I was younger, I had often expressed amazement when Dad would take down one of his many books and begin to read it. "How can you read a book about maths – what could you possibly find so interesting?" I had assumed they were the same as our schoolbooks, containing a few worked examples of a technique followed by hundreds of sample questions. The English in these schoolbooks is usually limited to words like *evaluate, simplify, verify, prove, show* ... so maybe you can see why I was at a loss to understand how anyone would wish to read such stuff.

One thing about Dad which I found a little annoying at first was his desire to know more about mathematicians. When I'd speak about interesting work I had just read by some mathematician or cryptographer, he would almost always ask, "Do you have a picture of him/her?" He says knowing a little about the people behind the maths can often make it more interesting. Students especially love to be told an anecdote which lightens a lecture or helps them remember a particular topic. Although I don't wish to give the impression that I never found a little history of mathematics or mathematicians of some interest, I did think Dad's curiosity a little excessive. However, having painstakingly gone through mathematical papers written by men and women who are alive as I write, and having read many popular articles about mathematics and cryptography, I now have a much keener interest in the human side. Recently I saw for the first time photographs of five men of whom I have heard so much and even talked about a little myself – Martin Hellman, Whitfield Diffie, Ron Rivest, Adi Shamir and Leonard Adleman. I must say that I was a little amazed to see these 'giants' in normal bodies. Now I hate to hear about the work of a mathematician without also being told a little about the person or seeing a picture of him or her. I am going to have to do something radical to stop myself turning into Dad!

In the end, the papers that helped me to show that the envisaged attacks were not computationally feasible turned out to be almost the very first ones I had read. But it took a long time before I could see clearly exactly what I had to do. I did an awful lot of jumping around and I indulged in many programming diversions. There were times when I could hardly think straight and often asked questions of myself which afterwards I could see were plainly stupid. But it all came together, culminating one evening in a "That's it!" which had me leaping with joy. Something had finally dawned on me, though it had been staring me in the face for a long time. I called a halt. I knew there was a lot more I could do, but I had enough in both senses: though I was mentally drained I now had a genuinely good extension of my '98 project, so Texas here I come!

I had never been to the USA before, so I was really looking forward to my visit to Fort Worth accompanied by my science teacher, Mr Foley. Intel paid for everything, which was absolutely great. We stayed in a hotel where I had a king-size room to myself for the week. My project was deeper, thanks to Michael Purser, and I just knew I was going to enjoy myself. The contestants ranged in age from fourteen to twenty-one. I was in the Mathematics category, and my stand was between those of two American boys. The fair was completely different in character from the Irish exhibition. Although it was definitely an international event, most of the contestants were American. In general, I found the participants to be very confident when speaking about their projects. Many of them, however, seemed to me to be overly so, and trying too hard to sell what they had done. Others had an air of knowing so much more than they did, and didn't fare too well when asked more probing questions. Some projects were obviously brilliant and did not need to be sold – they spoke for themselves. The displays were all very professionally done and were about twice the size of the ones at the Irish Young Scientist.

The biggest difference was in the judging process. There were nearly as many judges as contestants, and so the system was a complicated one. Each contestant received an appointment card with each fifteen-minute section of the judging day marked either 'open' or with a scheduled judge's name. Special award and additional regular judges could be expected during open periods. A bell rang at the end of each period, so there weren't going to be any judges talking to you for over half an hour, as they had been able to in Dublin. The morning before the first judging sessions, Frank Turpin, the 'man with the money' from Intel, took me shopping to take my mind off things. It worked, and we arrived back at the convention centre ten minutes before the judges started making their rounds at 12.15. I was not due a scheduled judge until 13.30, but I was judged right from 12.15 until 17.30 – no lunch break, no nothing! There was only one day of judging, and it was hectic. The questions asked were wide-ranging and varied. I was even asked about the difficulty of factorising large *primes*! I'll never forget that! It was the very slip of the tongue which I myself had made in one of my practice sessions. Dad had done a flip, saying that I'd be ruined if I ever made this mistake in public. At one point another judge came to see me with a notepad on which he had a whole list of questions written out. The judges had obviously collaborated before 'sending him in'. The questions were tough mathematical ones designed to make sure I was not bluffing. He got straight down to his task. I wrote out proofs for this and that, and explained certain concepts. When he went away smiling, I knew I could smile too. From the number of judges I had received I knew something was in the offing.

As it turned out, I was awarded a third-place Karl Menger Memorial Award from the American Mathematical Society and a fourth-place Grand Award in Mathematics, but more was to come. At the awards ceremony I remember laughing as the girl next to me jumped up into the air and ran towards the stage in a burst of excitement when her name was called out for a major prize. Mr Foley had also noticed her leap and we both laughed for her and at her show of delight. However, I certainly would have beaten her had there been a competition for who could jump the highest off a chair from a sitting position, for my name was called out next. I had felt so tense through the whole ceremony wondering if I would get any prizes, and having received two already I wasn't expecting any more in these final few minutes. To my complete surprise, at a time when

In Code

I thought I should be calming down, I instead found myself practically flinging my jacket at an innocent bystander who had been minding his own business by the steps to the stage. I was beaming as I received the $2000 Intel Fellows Achievement Award, and smiled as I thought of the two leaps that I and my fellow prize-winner had made just moments before. The evening and my trip to Texas were complete after that. I felt absolutely happy and content.

The minute I got back to my hotel room I rang Mom and Dad with all the news, delivering it, as ever, at a hundred miles an hour. I told Dad that the Americans were making a fuss over the 'new' algorithm, and I asked him to phone Dr Purser to tell him of the great reception I had received in Texas. I wanted also to give Michael credit by naming the algorithm the *Cayley–Purser algorithm*, Cayley for the matrices and Purser for the ideas. When he was told of this he said, "At my age I don't need recognition or awards." He was very kind and remarked that he was flattered at having his name linked to that of Cayley, saying this would be the second time he had been mentioned in "such distinguished company". An author friend, having expressed a certain view in his book, had added, "though Einstein and Purser will disagree with me".

Shortly after I had arrived back in Ireland I visited Baltimore Technologies with Dad. We were met by William, who introduced me to Michael, the man whose ideas I had worked on incessantly for weeks but had never met until now. I had brought two copies of my project report with me and gave one to each. Michael, who had a copy of his book *Introduction to Error-Correcting Codes* in his hand, on hearing that Dad lectured on this topic, immediately signed it and gave it to him. We all went for tea and cakes (which I was told William had gone to great lengths to procure), and I met again all those people I had got to know during my week's stay.

William and Michael were able to see the work I had done. I was extremely flattered by the compliments they paid me by email when they had read the report. But what delighted me, and was much more important to me, is that they took a keen interest. Michael in particular wrote many times with various suggestions.

Exhibition Time

I spent almost all of the summer on my grandparents' farm outside Killarney helping my aunt with the horses. In September I reluctantly returned to school for the fifth year to begin the two-year cycle for the Leaving Certificate examination. I had done no further work on my project, other than think about a number of plans I had for tying up loose ends which I hadn't been able to do before going to America. At Young Scientist '98 I had been encouraged to expand and improve upon my project for next year's competition. Clearly I could now do this with the material I had worked on for the Texas fair. However, rather than just expand it I decided to shed almost all of the old project, except for the portion which described the RSA. This, along with the new material, would be the basis of a fresh and deeper project which would focus solely on comparing and contrasting the RSA algorithm with what I was now calling the CP algorithm. The title of this project was to be 'Cryptography – A New Algorithm Versus the RSA'.

I was very pleased that I had kept records of all my work because they would help get me back to the frame of mind in which I could begin to tackle those questions which were still unanswered. I had two other ambitions: one to write crisper code (I knew my early stuff to be primitive in many respects); the other, if possible, to include a complexity analysis.

In my email correspondence with Michael and William there was a letter from Michael which discussed the possibility of explaining theoretically a figure I had obtained experimentally: the ratio of the times the CP algorithm and the RSA required for enciphering and deciphering. I found it intriguing that by thinking carefully about what an algorithm did while it was carrying out its tasks, and by making educated guesses as to how long each of the steps takes, one could hope to explain figures which were the results of practical tests. I imagined it to be almost like theoretical physics. Wouldn't it be fantastic if I could give reasons why the figures come out the way they do? So I was going to have a stab at this complexity analysis, though I had no illusions that it would be easy. It wasn't.

Circumstances helped to make writing better code almost painless. This year in the Mathematical Excursions class Dad was using *Mathematica* as a teaching aid. He had many examples prepared which showed all sorts of commands being used in very powerful ways. Seeing some of these commands used in ways slightly different from those I had used made me realise where I could make some of my procedures more efficient. Much time was devoted to dissecting superb code Dad had taken from programming books and admiring how cleverly it achieved its goals. I also began to look at code written by others, something I had done before but had found a little depressing because all that I read was simply too sophisticated. Understanding neater and more clever ways of doing things is a great thrill, even it does make you feel you are thick. I remember really admiring some code written by Stephen Kauffman of the ETH (the Eidgenössische Technische Hochschule, the Swiss Federal Polytechnic) in Zurich, which Dad had come across while at a *Mathematica* conference in Chicago in June 1998. It was written to implement the RSA system. Seeing how he tackled the enciphering and deciphering in a much more structured way showed me the wonderful flexibility of the *Mathematica* language. However, I often prefer to use my own code, even it's not state of the art, because I believe it corresponds to my way of thinking. At least then I have some chance of following what I wrote weeks ago when I re-read it. Of course, I do use and adapt ideas which make crude code less so.

I did a lot of work which I never reported because I didn't complete it. I failed to get the complexity analysis to a point where I could draw conclusions by which I could confidently stand. I wanted to include all that I had done to show how hard I had worked, but in the end I kept the report like the code, as crisp as I could manage. Despite not winning all the battles I had an original project, and with my thoughts clear in my head I felt ready and eager for Young Scientist '99.

Diary, Wed. 6th January 1999. Mr Foley and Vincent collected me from home close to 7.45 a.m. As usual, they were calm, but this was not how I was feeling. Normally I like getting excited about things, but on the journey to Dublin I was more tired than excited. I knew that the first judging session would be in the afternoon, so I was asking myself questions in my head and trying to anticipate what might really be asked. Got to the Royal Dublin Society (RDS) around noon. The hustle and bustle started the minute I arrived. Registered. Once I walked in the main door of the hall the atmosphere was overwhelming – a wave of noise and bright lights washed over me and I was filled with anticipation. It was very fun and professional at the same time. I felt as if I should be really cool and calm – after all, I was in the Senior section this year and had been here before. However, I was even more excited than last time, though I wasn't as nervous, as I knew what was supposed to happen. I set up my project and said hello to the people around me. I found out that Hugh Hurley's project was on the other side of my stand (Hugh's brother Raphael was last year's winner) and Vincent's was just two up from me, so I settled down. I set it up slowly and, again this year, it stood out as quite different. Some of the displays were really well done.

My first judge arrived earlier than expected, and I was disappointed that I wasn't more ready or tuned in. I had been talking to some of the other people at the stands around me and didn't have any time to myself to concentrate. I like to feel prepared, even if only the slightest bit. The judge was from Siemens – Dr Supple, a very nice man. I got the impression that he was not too interested in cryptography, but luckily it is a topic that can easily spark some interest in anyone if you try hard enough to explain what it is all about. I had a short introductory spiel prepared which I gave him. After being in America I had a better idea of how to mix their exuberant methods of explaining their projects with my idea of a good solid explanation – cover the most relevant points and expand on those which seem to interest the judges. Dr Supple stayed for about forty minutes, which was quite a long time. Even so, I don't feel I impressed him that much and I am disappointed that I did not get the chance to get into the nitty-gritty of the maths which, after all, is the core of my project. It was a good session overall but unfortunately not too probing. I want to show the judges that I can answer (or so I hope) whatever they throw at me, and I

In Code

hope that their questions will be mathematical in nature. Presumably the judges will understand that I do not have a knowledge of all the cryptographic ideas that have ever seen the light of day. I am always willing to learn and see no problem in the fact that I do not know as much as I might were I to read more widely. On the maths side of things I feel OK, though I know I could be asked questions which I cannot answer. It is hard to know to what depth to go.

At Young Scientist '98 I noticed that when people who knew something about cryptography came to my stand it was not with the aim of showing me up. Instead, they seemed anxious to show that they knew something about the topic. When they'd ask me what I thought of this latest development or that new idea, instead of attempting to answer (which sometimes I wasn't able to) I simply asked the person to elaborate. Suddenly, they would relax and become enthusiastic. This was a very interesting experience and a valuable lesson, though when a judge did something similar at last year's competition I found it a little unsettling. On one occasion a judge had proceeded to ask me questions about the Enigma machine*, and when I explained that it was not something I had studied in depth he started telling me about it as he settled himself comfortably into a chair. Let's just say that the middle of a judging session was not when I wanted to hear all this. He also asked me, "Do you really think that Julius Caesar invented or even used the Caesar cipher?" Now, that was one that even Dad, who I thought had asked me every question under the sun, hadn't thought of. I was glad when the judge eventually let me get back to talking about my project.

Thursday 7th. During breakfast, all I could think of was, "I am going to make an impression today." *Wenn Schön, denn Schön.* If you do something, do it right. I wouldn't disregard the modesty that my father and mother had instilled in me, but I would do my best to show the judges what I knew and what my project was all

---

*Used by the Germans during the Second World War to encode messages.

about. I really psyched myself up. It felt weird. Yesterday I had adopted a laid-back attitude, taking the judging as it came and not doing anything major to make it go where I wanted.

When we got to the RDS just after nine, a wave of tiredness swept over me because I didn't get to sleep last night until about four in the morning. It doesn't help that I have a very bad cold. I cleared away the copies of the previous day's edition of the *Irish Times* which had accumulated on the chair beside my stand and was about to sit down to clear my mind – yes, 'clear my mind', the very phrase I hate my father using – when I was met by a palm ready to be shaken and a very enthusiastic face indeed. It was my first judge of the day. I was suddenly awake. All my intentions since breakfast were fresh again at the top of my mind. The judge was Dr Eoin O'Neill, and I was delighted to see him. He had judged me last year and had given me the most satisfying grilling on every aspect of that project. He had even spoken to me again after the judging sessions were over, to encourage me to re-enter the following year, and he had given me a few tips. So this year I was going to show him that I had listened to his advice. I wanted to knock his socks off! I know it was the mathematics that impressed him last year and the fact that I know the basic concepts of public key cryptography. This meant that I could get right down to the main business of comparing and contrasting the new algorithm with the RSA. I could tell by his face that he was looking forward to hearing what I had to say, and that he would listen to every single word.

But then I realised that there was another palm waiting to be shaken and it belonged to a man whose face was unfamiliar. He looked as though he was aware that my judge was already here, yet he made no move to leave me and Dr O'Neill alone. Dr O'Neill introduced him simply as someone he had brought along with him as an external mathematician. So he was here to stay, and he was going to listen to my every word. Boy, was the heat on now! It felt really scary, yet a massive challenge to which I was dying to rise. I felt I had to live up to Dr O'Neill's obvious expectations, so I just started. Damn, it felt good! It was an excellent session. For over forty minutes I spoke as intensely as they listened. I wrote out each and every step of my beloved proofs on an A4 pad. I knew it would impress them more than if I simply slapped my report down on the desk and took them through it. I used Dad's horrid hand movements to explain certain concepts like homomorphisms and could see that they were watching every move I made. They listened intently as I wrote and explained the ideas and each step of my argument. At one point I just couldn't remember what I wanted to say next and told them I would get my report to show them some tables. Tables … that's it. I said, "Just before I do, I'll show you here on paper where I get what is in those tables." I could tell that this was one of the moments which impressed them most. I was delighted.

On one occasion I looked out of our little huddle and it felt really strange – our conversation was so very intense that just to look around was like coming up for air. I got a glimpse of Mr Foley, who was looking dead impressed and dumbfounded at the same time. I hate having people I know listen to me explain to others something I have already talked about with them. For a split second I felt very self-conscious, but once I leaned down on the desk again I was sucked back into our world. This must have looked very odd to anyone looking on: three of us all bent over, talking about maths proofs. They asked great questions (nothing about the difficulties of factorising large primes!). I delivered answers confidently and led them into other areas by expanding on certain points. I even talked about things I hadn't been able to figure out, such as the complexity analysis. Before they left, Dr O'Neill asked me the simplest question of all, and I could see that he was wondering whether or not I would be able to answer it. The answer was the fast exponentiation algorithm, and I must have smiled before I replied because I knew it was the perfect end to the perfect session. I had been able to defend my project at all levels. The last question was a check to see if I knew the fundamentals. They smiled at each other on my final answer, which I'll never forget. We shook hands again, and I hoped no one would get in my way as I ran to the phone booth, red-faced from exhaustion and excitement, to let off steam in a phone call to Mom and Dad which cost me an absolute fortune.

Exhibition Time

In the afternoon my third and final scheduled judge, Dr G. Frank Imbush, arrived around 3.30. His name rang a bell – I remembered Vincent talking about him last year, saying that he was one of the good judges, tough but fair. I didn't go into the mathematical side of the project on Dr O'Neill's advice of this morning, which was just as well as I have never been so mentally shattered. I still wanted to make an impression, but I was just so tired. The session went well but afterwards I felt that, of them all, this morning's was the only really good one. I feel badly about the other judging sessions because they were of a different standard. And yet I am not too worried, though my tired performance of this afternoon could, I think, have jeopardised my chances of a prize. But the session with the two judges was just so damn good – I still feel tingles of excitement thinking of it. It made me realise what a good intellectual conversation can be like – this morning's was one of the best ever and it was about maths. I am ready to go home, happy that I have done my best.

This evening I went to MacDonalds with Grandma and Grandad, and then to see the film *The Mighty* in Stillorgan. Afterwards I met friends, but all I could think about was that interview with Dr O'Neill, and that he had brought along an expert so that together they could ask me better questions. He is a good judge. What an extreme compliment that gesture paid me. I still don't know if I have lived up to his expectations. At the moment I feel that no one else could possibly understand the joy of such an interview or appreciate just how good a feeling I have about it. It is a lonely feeling but I don't mind. As long as I am happy within myself, that is more than a just reward.

I know that people cannot be expected to understand how I feel about the project, and it is probably for this reason that I do not like to be asked simply, "What is your project about?" It is not that I don't like to talk about it, but it cannot be explained fully in a few sentences. If I think someone isn't going to feel the same way about it as I do and just wants a superficial explanation, then I feel awful about trivialising it. That is not to say, however, that I do not respect or understand that not everyone gets a thrill from cryptography ideas. I like it that way – it makes it more special.

I forgot to ring Mom and Dad about that third judging session because I was so obsessed with the second one, which I still can't get over. I'll always remember that parting smile!

Friday 8th. Today I got more judges. If you get judges on the third day this means you are in the running, as they say, for a prize. This morning I had no such expectations – last year, when I won my category, I did not have any judges on the last day. So I began to feel quietly confident, thinking that, after all, this year's project is far better than last year's. The only point on which I still felt pessimistic was that I did not show what I feel to be an even level of ability when describing the project, so I thought a lot would rest on how respected Dr O'Neill's opinion was amongst the panel of judges. When Dr Supple came back with two more judges from other categories I was pretty pleased. He invited me to explain my project to them, which I was delighted to do. I had to express its merits without going into detail about what exactly they are. I explained things in simple terms – I had some straightforward props, such as the Caesar wheel, and I think they liked that in particular. I believe that nobody really minds being told something in a simple way. It is not an insult to anyone's intelligence and ensures that no one misses the point.

Later, Dr Supple came back with three more judges, and I knew that things were looking good. I took all this attention in my stride, though last year I would have died for it when I was sitting next to the boy who won. The first of this set of judges introduced himself as being from the group section – I thought he said group theory! Luckily I found out otherwise before I had him completely confused by speaking to him exclusively about my beloved proofs while appearing to ignore the others. It was a good session, but I was disheartened for a moment when one of the judges started looking around while I was speaking. In America they requested that judges appear to be interested in a student's project even if they think it to be trivial or uninteresting. They point out that the judging periods should build up the student's confidence in speaking on a topic in scientific or layman's terms. If one of my main judges had shown no interest I would have been deeply hurt. When I saw this particular judge look round I became distracted, and he upset my flow of thought and lessened my level of self-confidence. However, he seemed to tune back in again, and after a few nice questions on nothing too probing, the group left. I had looked over at one point during this interview and saw that my schoolmate Vincent too had judges. That was great! His father was leaning by the wall of the exhibition hall and was beaming with pride as he watched his son explain his project to his audience, which was obviously captivated.

Next thing I knew, judges from Intel came over. Then a judge from the Patent Office, followed by Dr Scott and, a little later, by Rev. Thomas Burke (who advised me to read Simon Singh's book, *Fermat's Last Theorem*). A few more judges called by, but I can't remember who they were. I know I had two judges from the Social and Behavioural category. While all this was happening Vincent also had more judges.

At 3.00 p.m. at least thirty of us were called backstage to wait for the closing ceremony, at which three individual and two group prizes would be awarded. My friend Raphael Hurley (the Young Scientist '98 overall winner) was also backstage, and he pointed out to me that besides myself there were only two other contestants with individual entries. All the others were group entrants, so according to Raphael most of them were 'spongers', which was his way of saying that they were there to fill out the set of possible prize winners. I didn't want to let myself believe that I was going to be one of the individual winners. When we were all called into a corridor right behind the stage, the televised ceremony got under way. Soon they would begin announcing the prize winners. It was then that Vincent was called up to the side of the stage and told that he was about to receive the Intel Award. A few moments later I was also called up, and Vincent told me his wonderful news. For one awful moment I thought I was only there as last year's Intel winner to present him with his prize. I was delighted for Vincent, but felt crushed inside. When Karina Howley (an Intel lady I know from last year) came over to the two of us and congratulated Vincent and then me, I went, "Hey, Karina, I don't know anything yet!" Two other guys from Intel, David and Ian, were beside the stage chatting away to me when an Esat girl came and took me backstage again to where all the 'groupies' were now settled. Vincent returned from his stint in front of the cheering audience. He was dead proud! Part of his prize was a trip to ISEF '99 in Philadelphia to be accompanied by his Dad as his teacher.

Karina's comment had set my mind spinning with excitement. Then Hugh Hurley and his team-mate Conor were called for the runner-up group prize. Next, two girls from Belfast were called to receive the overall group prize, followed by David Folan from Donegal as the individual runner-up. At this point I was the only individual entrant left backstage. I could hear the Taoiseach speaking about 'girl power' but I still would not let myself believe that I was to be the Young Scientist of the Year for 1999, winner of IR£1000 and Ireland's representative at the European Union Contest for Young Scientists at Thessaloniki, Greece, in September. It was just too scary.

The stage seemed enormous as I walked out to be presented by the Taoiseach with a magnificent trophy. I remember talking to him for a while, and afterwards there were lots of photographs taken. The rest is just a blur.

7. After-math

In the rush of photographs, interviews and handshakes that followed backstage after receiving the award, I don't believe I got one moment to myself to step back from it all and let what had just happened sink in. "Sarah, are you delighted with your win?" But of course I'm delighted – I just don't feel delighted yet. When I eventually got past the wall of attention after interviews with Radio Television Eireann Television News and International News Network, I was met by Mom's smiling face and those of my brothers Michael and Brian. At that stage what I would have most liked was to talk to Mom and Dad about the events of the last few hours. However, Dad had remained at home with my two younger brothers, David and Eamonn, but even if he had been there I could hardly have unwound just then as my voice was almost gone because of all the talking.

The 18.01 bulletin and later the nine o'clock news that Friday night reported on the competition in general. They both showed a clip describing the nature of my project and its possible applications. This was followed by a short interview with me and then one with a judge, who commented, "If she plays her cards right I think she should make a lot of money …".

Saturday morning's papers gave a lot of coverage to the Young Scientist Exhibition with photographs of some of the contestants and descriptions of projects. As overall winner I certainly got a fair share of publicity, with photographs of me appearing on the front pages of some of the national papers. The *Irish Times* carried the article with the headline JUDGES DESCRIBE WINNER'S PROJECT AS 'BRILLIANT' and a picture of Mom and me underneath. Other papers also had very flattering headlines along with paragraphs discussing the project. One, under a section heading 'Huge Implications', read,

> She tackled the encryption of messages as used by banks, business and governments to safeguard information. The security of these messages is vitally important for business, particularly where credit card and smartcard transactions are concerned. Her new computer system could have huge implications for the industry.

My display had been moved from its stand up to the main stage immediately after the award ceremony, and for the entire weekend it was absolutely swarming with people wanting to see 'the winning project'. Many stayed for a long time reading it, some even took notes. Although I wondered what they made of it all, I spent most of the time out of sight as I was shattered.

That night in the hotel I was to meet all my Dublin relations – my three uncles with their families and my grandparents – and of course Mom, Michael and Brian. I remember asking Mom whether or not Dad might come to Dublin that day or the day after. I was really disappointed if not a little annoyed when she said she didn't think he would. Later, when I saw him walking in with my two younger brothers to the room where we were all gathered, I rushed over to him, hugged him and said, on the point of tears, "I'm so glad you're here, I've had nobody to talk to." After drawing him to one side I gushed technical talk for at least a quarter of an hour; what I couldn't discuss with others I now poured out. As I spoke I could feel the tension leave my body and relief slowly take over. Only later in the bathroom when I burst into tears of happiness did I realise that all the praise and admiration meant nothing until I had spoken about the real reasons I had won the competition. After that private conversation I really began to enjoy myself, and I had a great time joshing with my sharp-witted uncles who were determined not to let me get a big head.

After-math

One very funny thing happened just as we all stood up to say goodnight. When I went over to Dad I surprised myself so much by what I did that I just broke down laughing, along with everyone else who saw me. I unconsciously stuck out my hand to be shaken. Dad gave me a puzzled look, but it is only when he took my hand that I realised what I had done. I still cannot believe that I did that. I must have shaken a hundred people's hands in the last day and a half and was just programmed by that stage. I turned off automatic pilot and gave Dad a proper goodnight hug, but I shall never forget that moment as a reminder of just how mentally tired it had all made me.

The following morning, Sunday, the major award winners met President McAleese at her official residence, Áras an Uachtaráin. I was allowed to bring my four grandparents along with Mom. Dad's mother had an irrepressible smile on her face for the entire visit and when the President was introduced to my mother's father he brought the conversation around, as only he can do, to a discussion of the trophy I had been given. He informed her that while its silver top in the shape of a tetrahedron had three different scientific themes carved into its faces, its base is made from 4800-year-old Irish bog yew – something which we all agreed was humbling and which makes it very special.

Later that afternoon, back at the exhibition hall, I couldn't help but smile on overhearing someone say, "And to think that people spend thousands of pounds to send their children to posh schools!" I knew that Vincent and I had to be in some way the subjects of this conversation, and I felt pleased for our teachers that this was one of the reactions to our school's double victory.

I must admit that I was a little uneasy about going back to school because I was unsure what the reaction of my friends and fellow students might be. Would they suddenly not want to talk to me because they thought me a swot? If so, that was their problem. But I was just being paranoid. When Vincent and I arrived back for classes our fellow pupils and teachers were proud and thrilled, and regarded us as two heroes returning to their school. One of the nicest things anyone said to me, strangely enough, was a simple but sincere "Fair play to ya, girl" (actually it was "Fair f**ks to ya, girl!", but anyway). Later in the week village pride peaked when the media reported on the Taoiseach's visit to Blarney to congratulate the school for its achievements and for its Young Scientist double. The importance of this unprecedented occasion really rubbed off on everyone and gave the whole place a lift. It was a very memorable day.

This was the first of a number of events at which I was to be made aware of the appreciation that Cork people show when one of their own makes them proud. About a month after the Young Scientist exhibition I was invited to a gala dinner by the organisers of the information technology exhibition, IT@Cork. I thought I was only there for the photographs, but they had a surprise in store for me. In the main speech they spoke of the aims of their exhibition, one being to publicise the development of IT in Cork. To that end they announced that they wished to present me with a laptop as a way of expressing their pride in my putting Cork on the IT map. A laptop! That is the biggest material present I have ever received.

Later I was made a Cork Person of the Month, and later still I was given a civic reception by the Lord Mayor, which makes me very proud to be a Cork person.

The day before the Taoiseach's visit an article had appeared on the front page of the London *Times* which (as mentioned already in the Preface) carried a large photograph of me in front of a blackboard and a caption underneath which read:

Sarah Flannery, 16, who baffled the judges with her grasp of cryptography. They described her work as 'brilliant'.

This article changed my life. Had it been placed somewhere in the inside pages of the paper as originally intended, then I believe that you would not be reading this book now. Reuters picked up on the story, and my name along with a summary of what I was supposed to have achieved was published in newspapers all around the world. This caption, while flattering, left me completely flabbergasted. I could not believe that a school project could evoke such interest and

After-math

I could barely take in the fact that the article was about me and not some other person.

Within hours of its first appearance press, radio, TV, Internet surfers, patent lawyers and well-meaning individuals assailed our home by phone, email and letter. On that day alone we received sixty phone calls! For weeks afterwards Dad had to remain at work late into the evenings to answer the flood of emails enquiring about my project. This was just the beginning. Our old farmhouse has a lane leading up to it so long and bumpy that we are rarely visited, even by the most eager canvassing politicians. However, this border road between our privacy and the outside world proved no obstacle to the stream of enthusiastic reporters from all over, who were to brave its horrors over the next few weeks to ask me questions.

It was unavoidable that William and Michael too would be sought out to express their opinion of me and/or what I was supposed to have achieved. As soon as the *Times* story broke, William received the following email from an English colleague:

```
From the front page of today's Times <www.the-
times.co.uk>. As usual (technically) content free.
Anyone know any technical details?
```

The opening lines of William's reply were:

```
Yes, I do. It's based on work that Sarah did in
Baltimore when she was here on a student work
placement last March.
```

These were followed by some explanatory technical paragraphs. He finished by writing:

```
I haven't had time to look at Sarah's project in great
detail so I don't know how far (or even whether) she's
taken it beyond where we had it.
   Sarah, by the way, is level-headed enough to know
that new public key algorithms only made you millions
```

```
if you invented them in the Seventies. Her real
problem is trying to stop the journalists talking up
the stupid parts of the story while still emphasising
that there's a real story in there.
```

Later in the evening he wrote:

```
In fact, Sarah made substantial contributions to the
development of the algorithm, finding a way of trading
off key generation time against encryption time and
doing a lot of work on the proof of security. It's
very impressive.
```

The *Guardian* newspaper published an article headed TALES FROM THE ENCRYPT and quoted Michael as saying the following:

And this lassie Sarah Flannery came to do work experience from school. It was immediately perceived that she could do more than the tea, and they said can you programe [sic]? and when she said yes, they said: "Why don't you try and programe [sic] this idea of Michael Purser's?" So that is what she did. She did it in three days, which was remarkable.

She's a charmer: she wins the hearts of everybody who meets her, she's slightly shy and very modest and very concerned to give credit to other people, and she has a lovely smile and long hair and she's anything but brash. But she's very sharp. If you say something to her, she doesn't accept it like that, she analyses it. She has a very good brain and a determination to understand, to make sense of what she is doing.

Knowing from my own experience that what is printed is often not exactly what was said, I was nevertheless delighted. How could I not be?

At the end of the week of the *Times* article the phone calls were still coming. Friday night, as I was about to leave for the annual athletics club dinner (which I was really looking forward to), the phone rang again. How I resisted the temptation to let it ring and just walk out the door I do not know. It was phone call number 147 of the week, and I was in no mood to talk to anyone except my athletics buddies over a really good meal. "Hello, may I speak to Ms Sarah Flannery please?" My speaking was answered by the caller identifying himself. "This is Ron Rivest calling. I wonder if I may have a few moments of your time to speak with you?" I couldn't believe my ears. All I could muster was "Excuse me?" At first I thought it was Dad fooling around. It could have been but it wasn't. I couldn't believe I was speaking to Professor Rivest from MIT, the R in the RSA. I was *very* nervous and felt so humble speaking to him. At the same time I didn't want to sound like someone who couldn't stand her ground. He wanted to talk mathematics and I was delighted to do so, no matter how uneasy the experience was making me. It was so satisfying to be asked questions by someone who would not expect trivialised answers. Having such a conversation after days of being asked to spell 'algorithm' was very fulfilling. Ronald Rivest – wow!

In an interview later, when asked about me, he kindly said, "She knows her number theory." This is high praise, coming from a man who was instrumental in developing one of the first practical applications of number theory. A remark like this, though to my mind too great a compliment, is a lot more gratifying than being described as a mathematical genius by someone who could not have an appreciation of what that really means.

After the Ron Rivest phone call I went to the dinner and had an enjoyable time. The food and the company were great – they even presented me with a huge cake. But I couldn't wait to share my recent phone call with my parents, who were in England at an aunt's fortieth birthday party. The next morning, when I contacted them, Dad could not believe who had phoned. My uncle, having heard the shouts during our conversation, asked why Dad was so excited. Upon being told, he commented, "I take it then, that God has been in touch."

One issue that sent a lot of people into a tizzy was ignited by the sentence

In Code

She is considering publishing her findings rather than patenting as she does not want people to pay for her discovery.

This appeared in the second-to-last paragraph of the infamous *Times* article, which appeared under the headline TEENAGER CRACKS E-MAIL CODE.

"Are you going to patent it?" was a question I was asked by almost everyone. And almost everyone had an opinion which they were anxious to share with me whether I wished it or not. Judging from some of the Internet sites, the issue sparked off a war of words. The following extracts are a very small sample of the many views expressed:

God Bless this kid for not patenting her discovery.

Yeah yeah ... wonderful things, she's already won one for the young people, etc. etc. ... Newsbreak for little Sarah – none of that crap pays the bills. If she's reading this then the message is simple – patent this! You're a genius and you deserve to be paid for it.

A very intelligent but naive girl. She should patent the information and license it. If she finds the rest of her life as productive as her teens, she could let it go for as little as she feels necessary.

I hope Sarah's parents are wise enough to talk her into a patent. While her attitude is an applaudable one, it would behoove her to retain the right to such a potentially profitable technical development. What they haven't taught young Sarah in science class just yet is that most scientific discoveries don't get patented because they have no profit potential, not because scientists are more altruistic than anyone else as a group.

Don't ever underestimate Sarah's contribution to the world. I am not only talking about the faster data transfer; I am also talking about the generosity and her down-to-earth attitude. Just imagine how much we have been paying for the patent royalties; some of them are reasonable; some of them not. Of course, one may argue, without patent protection, no one would spend anything on R and D. True. But hey, Sarah deserves our praise for her generosity.

The most important thing to come out of this, besides faster encryption, is the message it sends to young people, and especially young women, around the world ... Those who worry that she might 'lose' because she has chosen not to patent her algorithm are missing the point, which is that she has already 'won'.

Well done – good to see somebody not in it for a fast buck!!

Make money Sarah! Patent it! Don't throw away millions of dollars!!!!

It is very telling to see from whence came the criticism of this young lady's decision not to patent her discovery. The American Dream is to invent something, live off its profits, and never think or work another day in one's life. That is why Bill Gates is such an American hero. It is presumptuous and arrogant to think that this girl who has achieved so much in so little time does not understand the 'ways of business' ... Also, her fame is greatly enhanced by making her breakthrough freely available. I congratulate Sarah on her achievement! She is very cool.

Great achievement, if it is proved to be of both encryption strength and high speed. Her idea of not patenting it reminds me of the essence of science, explore the world and share the discovery. Cool.

Her act is in the true spirit of the Internet.

Sarah – Remember a woman's perogative – you can change your mind.

Patent it. Okay? Cool.

Software patents are extremely short-sighted. Imagine if great thinkers such as Sir Isaac Newton or Albert Einstein had been more concerned about protecting their IP [intellectual property] than advancing the collective body of knowledge of humanity. Every textbook that talked about the fundamental laws of motion or general relativity would be that much more expensive because of the licensing fee. I'll give you an example: how many people outside of the sphere of mathematics have heard of the Kalmann filter? This is one of the most significant breakthroughs in recent history, yet it has not achieved the degree of awareness of say the Theory of General Relativity. I argue that this is due in part to the fact that it was patented.

Before the competition I had never given any serious consideration to the commercial potential of my project. We certainly discussed the issue of patenting, but Dad's strong feeling was that mathematical ideas ought to be freely shared by all. To do otherwise would be an insult to the memory of the great mathematicians of the past, who carefully recorded their ideas so that future generations could build on them. So I gave the matter no further thought and just concentrated on my work.

When Michael visited the Young Scientist hall on the final Sunday afternoon of the exhibition, he handed me a letter in which he set out his thoughts on the patent issue. Kind as ever, he had written that should I wish to patent my project, as some had urged me to do, then it was a decision for me and my parents and he would undertake to make no objections. In the letter he advised strongly against trying to patent, believing, like many, that it would be immoral.

Where would we be if Lanczos had patented his method for solving linear equations with sparse matrices? If Pollard had patented his number field sieve? If Box and Jenkins patented their linear predictor? Mathematicians should be above such mercenary nonsense!

He also questioned whether or not the algorithm *could* be patented.

After-math

It had been on display at the exhibition, which had been open, if briefly, to the public. He pointed out that there are many *free* encryption algorithms, so why would someone pay me rather than use one of these? Furthermore, to make a commercial success of the algorithm I'd need to market it worldwide and submit it to standardisation bodies (more time and expense), with very uncertain prospects of any eventual payback.

Since my project had been on public display, all this do/don't patent talk was a load of stable-door locking after the horse had bolted. Had I stressed this last point more in interviews I might not have found myself on the 'altruistic high-ground' where the media placed me. Michael's and Dad's views and my agreement with them were not the *only* reasons I gave for not patenting. However, the press chose to emphasise my more high-minded comments and often omitted the more practical reasons.

Many therefore found my refusal to cash in on the overnight fortune they were certain I could earn, utterly incomprehensible.

WHO WANTS TO BE A MILLIONAIRE ... I DON'T
Sarah spurns a fortune.

This newspaper front-page headline and caption, and ones like them, were a pain.

I didn't like the idea of appearing a fool to all the people who 'wouldn't say no' to an inward cash-flow boost (actually I'm a loyal member of this club), and I didn't want my parents to be viewed as not protecting their daughter's best interests. All I could do was laugh when I heard "Are you going to become a billionaire?" or "I've heard rumours at work that you're worth 3.4 million already" or "Is it true that you've signed a deal worth 23 million pounds with some technology company?" I wish. I wish. I wish.

Had I wanted to patent I would have no shortage of advice or financial backing. I got many letters from patent lawyers like this one:

We would be prepared to handle the patenting of the encryption method in return for a negotiable fixed percentage of royalties received from the licensing of those patents ... Ownership of all patent rights would remain with you at all times, and our firm would have no proprietary interest in the intellectual property rights.

This same firm, offering unsolicited "venture capital advice", said in an email to my father that they were "horrified to see that she is considering publishing it without staking a claim to her intellectual property".

Within a matter of weeks, patenting the CP algorithm would be ruled out even more strongly, though it remained an issue in the public mind for many months. However, this is a story which must wait until I deal briefly with another issue of 'perception' which for me was more worrying.

My parents' reaction to all that happened to me after the Young Scientist competition was one of mixed feelings. They were of course delighted with my win but had grave concerns about many things, in particular the 'genius' label. They were afraid of the consequences for me of an exaggerated assessment of my intelligence being accepted as fact, and were anxious that I should not be blown out of proportion as this could only be a burden on me. They warned me continually to stick to the truth and not to allow myself be manipulated so that I'd be perceived as someone other than I am. "Don't let people make assumptions about you" is a statement I was later to hear from an IBM executive in Milan, and that pretty well hits the nail on the head.

I have no doubt that I am not a genius. I am not being falsely modest. Through my father's classes I have seen examples of true genius, and I know that I do not possess that 'insight' that distinguishes geniuses from those regarded as merely intelligent. I also know of their complete dedication to and obsession with their interests. But they possess that extra vital 1 per cent in Thomas Edison's quote, "Genius is one per cent inspiration and ninety-nine per cent perspiration." I was fortunate to be interested in my project topic. Although I was interested – very interested – and worked very hard, I would never say that I was obsessed to the point of losing sleep.

After-math

It is not always easy to keep a grip on reality when people are assuring you that what you have done is out of the ordinary and that it merits the description of genius. You even grow tired of telling them to steady on and not go overboard. What's more, you wonder if they think you are play-acting by making a pretence at false modesty. Deep down, though, you know that all this genius talk is a load of old blarney. I don't constantly dream of mathematics or cryptography to the exclusion of all else: I'm as often thinking about when I can next arrange to visit my aunt and her horses, or I'm on the phone to hear what my friends are up to.

How did my four brothers, Michael (fifteen), Brian (thirteen), David (ten) and Eamonn (seven), react to all the fuss? The two older boys have been consistently coy. On the day I won the Young Scientist award I remember asking Mom, "Where are the boys?" She told me they were hiding behind poles so as to avoid being caught by a photographer. Later they grew to resent any media intrusion into their lives, and disappeared whenever necessary. On one occasion when Dad asked Michael to join a family shot, exhorting him to "Do it for Sarah", Michael replied, "Dad, this isn't for Sarah, this is for *them*." Dad let him be, asking only that, the next time he took a 'stand' on an issue, it be a little more serious in nature. I don't want to make Michael out to be a grouch – he's far from it. He doesn't mind my doing interviews or photos and he's interested to see articles about me – he just doesn't see what *he* has to do with anything. That's OK. When he's a famous rock-star, I won't get into a photo with him. He made sure that all the attention didn't go to my head, without of course going over his daily limit of ten words. "You're seriously overrated, you are." The extra 'you are' was for emphasis. Brian liked to appear indifferent but always wanted to know what was happening. His main concern about all the attention and publicity was that we'd all be seen as getting above ourselves. With his usual frankness he allowed himself to remark, "People will think we're posh gits." Charming!

My two younger brothers, David and Eamonn, didn't let any macho egos get in the way of telling their 'big sister' how proud they were of her. They never resented any of the attention that surrounded us all for a while. In fact, two more forthcoming interviewees were never interviewed, nor were more willing subjects ever photographed. They loved all the excitement and insisted on helping the TV camera men by carrying their very expensive equipment. The CBS crew were so taken by something Eamonn said about the persistent 'buuurrp, buuurrp, …, buuurrp, buuurrp' of the telephone that they included him in their piece, which is something that made him very proud.

It wasn't always fun for the 'two smallies'. There were times when Mom, Dad and I were so busy that the younger boys didn't get their usual quota of attention and were lucky to be read their bedtime story. More often than not they were left in the care of their two older brothers, for whom the basic rule of society is that 'might is right'. Yet they never complained, and took it all in their stride.

About a month after my Young Scientist win I was approached by an advertising agency representing Pepsi Cola to do a billboard advertisement. The amount of money being offered would keep me going for a whole year in university, all for a few hours' 'work' in a photo shoot, so when Mom and Dad advised me strongly against doing the ad I felt frustrated. Their seeming unwillingness to make a penny out of my success contrasted with the way newspaper and magazine companies and photographers were benefiting from my fame. I had never asked any one of them for money, nor was any ever offered.

Admittedly, I wasn't keen on seeing my face plastered on billboards, but it had already been all over the newspapers, so that wasn't going to be an objection. "It's innocent," I argued, "it's an ad for a soft drink, not cocaine!" My parents weren't convinced. They were afraid that I would be seen as a Pepsi girl rather than as a young scientist, and that my achievement might be trivialised as a result. Maybe. They might have considered an ad with a health theme along the lines 'it's not smart to do drugs or smoke', but their fundamental objection to the proposed ad which I found most telling would be the big lie that I drink Pepsi exclusively. Even if the ad didn't quite imply this, it would still be a lie for me to claim that I think Pepsi the *best* of all the coke drinks, and even if the ad didn't say this either, it might suggest, however indirectly, that Pepsi makes you clever enough to win science contests. This would obviously be a lie, and though I know it's not the same thing as saying 'clever people drink Pepsi', advertisers know that we don't always distinguish between a statement and its converse. I wouldn't mind doing an ad for something I know about and believe to be worthwhile. I would have no hesitation, for instance (and I wasn't asked to say this), in recommending the mathematical package *Mathematica*, because I have used it many times and find it wonderful. I'd be prepared to say this and wouldn't say 'No' to an offer of money for doing so.

Another well-known 'company' who were very much taken by my success was none other than The Spice Girls. Their promotion company phoned Mom one day seeking permission to include me in their magazine. Mom thought this was charming and a bit of fun, and said yes. Dad's students, who had been very politely deferential about my Young Scientist success, abandoned all reticence and were full of interest and questions when they read 'Smart Spice – Pop Babes Think Irish Whizzkid Has Girl Power'. The males in particular wanted to know if they could be 'fixed up' – with a Spice Girl, of course, not me!

Among the many communications I received was a series of four-to-five-page handwritten letters which, when deciphered, proved to be proposals to set up a company. Typically they detailed everything about the new company the author and I would form together. The advantages and disadvantages were laid down clearly, though naturally there never were any real disadvantages to speak of! Sources of capital were no problem. I could get back to my schoolwork, equity funds would be set up, my parents could be directors, and so on. The wackiest letter I got contained – along with other curious statements – the following:

> We can split the codes stocks. I want to keep 53% (I was born in 1953) because you are a minor and your parents can (if they want) be co-vice presidents/co-consultants in the new code company ...

Mom replied very delicately to this letter and didn't mention what I would have been unable to resist pointing out – that I was born in 1982!

Only once did I meet someone in person who wished to discuss the possibility of forming a cryptography company. About two days after the *Times* article had appeared I was in Dad's office in CIT surfing the net for papers while waiting for him to return from a meeting. The phone rang, and the caller, speaking with an American accent, very slowly asked if he could speak with David Flannery. I explained that he was not available and suggested that I might do. (Every phone call Dad had that week was from somebody enquiring about me.)

When Dad returned to the office just minutes later, I – excited as ever – told him of the phone call I had just had. The caller had said that he was phoning from London in the hope that he might meet both my parents and me in a few hours' time. He elaborated by saying that he was a businessman who formed companies based on intellectual ideas, and he mentioned the names of one or two which sounded familiar but didn't register with me that strongly. I was preoccupied with wondering how he saw himself getting to Ireland, never mind Cork, in such a short space of time. When he went on to say that he had a private jet and that he could meet us later that evening at some hotel of our choosing, I was bowled over. Recovering some composure, I asked him to phone our home in an hour's time.

The conversation Mom, Dad and I had at the kitchen table that evening about the impending visit of one so rich that he didn't depend on commercial airlines was unlike any other we had had in the past. We decided that it could do no harm to meet him; if nothing else it would be fun and it was sure to be informative. We even wondered if it was all a spoof, but when he phoned again as promised we made an appointment to meet him at 7.30 in the Blarney Park Hotel a kilometre or so from our home.

As Dad and I sat in the foyer waiting for the arrival of our visitor, we wondered as each male entered through the glass door, "Is this he?" Will he be on his own or will he be accompanied by a group of business types in smart suits? Dad of course was his usual casual self in regard to dress – just about passable but with his hair barely combed (which Mom says is far worse than not combed at all).

The American arrived on his own by taxi – a short, white-haired man impeccably dressed and close to sixty years of age. After introducing ourselves we made our way into the restaurant, which was very quiet, and seated ourselves as far as possible from the few other diners so that we could speak in relative privacy. The American ordered a fish plate, while Dad and I had coffee as we had just eaten. Our visitor began by telling us a little about himself as a businessman and then as a family man. Although he had left us in no doubt that he was fabulously wealthy, he was at pains to point out that one of his sons, after trying a career in business, had found his true vocation as a research worker and was now happy living on what he earned. He mentioned that all his children had been educated at home before going to university. That was something I knew would impress Dad a lot – let's just say Dad has very unorthodox views on education. Our guest then enquired a little about us.

It was at least twenty minutes before he started to talk about the purpose of his visit. He explained again that he seeks out inventors, intellectuals with promising ideas, with a view to setting up companies around them. Those with the ideas are made major shareholders but are very much left to continue doing what they do best, while the day-to-day running of the company is done by people skilled in management. When Dad asked if he could be described as a venture capitalist, he became, I think, a little offended. He was keenly interested in seeing ideas reach their commercial potential and saw himself as much more than someone who just invested money to make more money. Needless to say, he was interested in the CP algorithm. He had read about it offering just as much security as existing standards and that, being twenty times as fast, it was set to revolutionise private communication on the Internet.

Until a fortnight before this meeting the CP algorithm was just part of a school project. Even if I had reported on its security and speed, I had never thought about exploiting it in a commercial way. As I said in answer to a question about patenting, "Why would someone pay me for an algorithm when there are so many freely available?" Even now, with all the uncritical praise for the algorithm and its potential, I had never seen it as entirely belonging to me, though I must admit that at that very moment I would have dearly loved to be responsible for it from beginning to end, and to be absolutely sure that it was as secure as my investigations claimed it to be.

But I wasn't solely responsible for the algorithm. My project is based on an idea of Michael's which I encountered at Baltimore Technologies, so should it have commercial potential, Michael and Baltimore would have to be in on it. In fact, because of all the hype surrounding the algorithm I was due to visit Baltimore the following weekend to discuss with them how best to handle all the publicity we were both receiving. Our visitor asked us a few questions about the company and I explained my connection. It was clear that he had done his homework because he knew that they were in the process of merging with another cryptography firm.

Although I didn't want to chase our visitor away without hearing what he had to say, and without getting some glimpse into the world of high finance, I felt I had to point out to him that the algorithm which was the reason for his visit had not, at this early stage, received any extensive form of peer review. I explained that such a process must be undergone before any algorithm is established as being satisfactorily secure; and that, while the judges had said in their citation "the demonstration of why the code is secure is publishable" and the external mathematician had been very impressed with the mathematics, neither he nor the judges, as far as I knew, were cryptographers. I also told him that Baltimore were much more circumspect in their statements about the algorithm than the media, because as experienced cryptographers they know that the wayside is littered with countless failed cryptosystems which once held promise. As a reputable company Baltimore didn't wish to pronounce on the CP algorithm without giving it a thorough examination, now that it was receiving such attention and being associated indirectly with them.

I don't know what he made of all of this candour. It didn't appear to upset him in any way, though I wondered whether he was beginning to think his whole journey a wasted one. I told him that I had made all these cautionary comments to reporters, but the articles they then wrote omitted them for fear, I speculated, that they put a dampener on a wonderful story.

He listened very attentively, and spoke in very general terms about how one would form a cryptographic company, while mentioning sums of money which seemed to be in multiples of billions rather than millions. After about forty minutes I noticed that he was starting to begin sentences with "We". This was scary. It made me feel as if I had somehow committed myself to something when I hadn't. At one point he casually asked what the combined worth of Baltimore and their prospective partners might be. "About 700 million dollars?" he speculated, and continued by saying that it would only be a matter of "our" buying them out. Whew! He wasn't being boastful, just matter of fact. When Dad said that I owed everything to Dr Purser and couldn't dream of talking about commercial ventures without first seeking his opinion, he remarked, "We'd look after the good doctor." I didn't quite know what to make of this, but it didn't sit well with me. Dad nearly had a heart attack when our visitor asked to accompany us on our visit to Baltimore. As politely as he could, Dad said that though his suggestion might seem very business-like, it was completely out of the question for a number of reasons, most of which were to do with good manners and friendship. Can you imagine what it would have looked like if I had arrived at Baltimore with a hard-nosed American businessman acting as though he were protecting my interests? It was a relief to talk him out of such a crazy notion without being rude. But he was very interested in exploring the possibility of exploiting the algorithm. We left him in no doubt that if such a thing were ever to take place it would have to be with Baltimore, and parted with a promise to phone him after our weekend visit.

The conversation had lasted well over an hour. As we were all leaving the hotel I was surprised to see him approach a local man as if he knew him. He did. It was the taxi driver who had brought him to Blarney waiting to take him back to Cork Airport and his private jet, which was on standby to take him to Nice in the south of France. Wow!

On the way home we talked a little about the problem of selling somebody a secret. How do you sell a secret to someone without that person getting to know it before he has paid you, and how does the person who is buying it know that he is getting the real thing?

At the end of the week I visited Baltimore, and was warmly received and congratulated on my Young Scientist win. More cake was had by all. Afterwards William and I spoke about the issues that arose from the unexpected publicity that the company and I had received. William kindly remarked that Baltimore had got ten times more publicity through their association with me than they had received some months previously through their involvement with the first 'digital-signing' of an agreement between President Clinton of the USA and our Taoiseach, Mr Ahern. He also joked that each mention of Baltimore on the front page of a newspaper was worth about IR£30,000. I must send them a bill.

We discussed examining the CP algorithm in more detail now that the world had taken more than a passing interest. We thought perhaps that I and Baltimore should (when we both had time) prepare a paper with a view to publishing it in a journal or, failing that, post my project report on a Web page with a commentary based on our subsequent findings. There was no talk of making millions, and as far as they were concerned I was free to talk to whomever I liked about whatever I liked, write whatever books I wished provided I promised to say nice things about them, and go into business with whomever I liked.

Almost immediately after the meeting I phoned the mobile number I had been given by the American visitor, but I couldn't get through. I checked with directory enquiries, national and international, but to no avail. The following Wednesday he phoned and I read him back the number I had taken down. I had been missing a digit. I apologised for appearing indifferent but told him of my attempts to contact him. We spoke for a few minutes about all sorts of possibilities. He was to 'get back', but as yet I have heard nothing. Was he for real?

By the end of January I had spoken with over three hundred journalists from newspapers, magazines, Web sites and TV. I never refused to do an interview – I spoke to everyone. Not all the phone calls I received were from journalists and some I would not have wished to miss, like those with invitations to take part in events in places as far away as Singapore.

I also did many radio interviews for stations such as Radio Columbia in South America (that was an interesting one – parallel translation), and Greek, French, German, American, South African, English and of course Irish stations. Those interviews *as Gaeilge* (in Irish) put me on the spot. My Irish can't be described as fluent and I knew my teacher would be listening in, ready to take down all my mistakes for the next class. Interviews for magazines were usually the longest and often led to two- or three-page spreads, some of which I never saw. The interviewers were usually well prepared with questions and lots of clippings for me to comment on. One German reporter, on hearing that Dad and I were off to the Mathematical Excursions evening class, asked if he could come along. He wanted to witness Dad's lecturing and experience the atmosphere. He sat next to me for one and a half hours and seemed to take a keen interest. He must have enjoyed his trip back to school because he wrote a glowing piece for his Hamburg newspaper.

Because I am self-conscious when it comes to any kind of camera I hated having to appear on television. I found such appearances so tiring and stressful that I swore, "Never again!" after I had done three or four of them. An Irish and a German TV crew filmed at home and at school for one and a half days each. Filming at school was the worst. "Just ignore us." Ya! Right! Whatever! The crew would walk behind me into classes and follow me through the corridors with their big black cameras. I worried what my classmates or others in the school might think, but some did seem to lap up the attention. A team from CBS News's *48 Hours* programme filmed me for three days at home, in the Mathematical Excursions class in CIT, at school, horse-riding in Blarney Castle grounds, playing basketball, even eating my dinner. Although they were extremely considerate, very soon it all got too much for me and I just wanted to run away and hide.

I received many invitations from universities and colleges around the country to give lectures on the CP algorithm. These talks were meant to be specific in nature, and presented at maths department seminars or meetings of student mathematical and computer societies. At the time I was so snowed under that Dad kicked for touch on my behalf on most of these flattering offers. However, I received two invitations which I simply couldn't refuse, and a third which I accepted for reasons I'm still not sure of, but which I think had something to do with seeing if I had enough nerve.

Very early on I received an invitation to Singapore. I and one of my parents were to be guests of the government for an all-expenses-paid trip. In return I was to give a speech at the closing ceremony of their National Science Talent Search Contest, and give a number of talks at some of their secondary schools to groups of young people of my own age. The rest of the time (which was a whole week) was my own, and they'd throw in some spending money. Even if I were the shyest person in the world I wasn't going to turn this one down!

I was also invited by IBM EMEA (Europe, Middle East and Asia) to be an external guest speaker at their first ever leadership conference for women. The conference, in Milan, had the theme 'Women and Technology in the New Millennium'. Apparently I was wanted as a speaker because I was an example of "the highly intelligent, motivated and determined young women who are set to change the face of our industry in the years ahead". Oh! Imagine what an expert-in-everything the audience would be expecting on seeing such a description in the programme. Very intimidating, but again the invitation was more than generous. I and both my parents would be put up in a fancy hotel, and be chauffeur driven to and from all events, and I would receive a fee for speaking which ranked (from my point of view) with some of the numbers used in cryptography.

The third invitation was to be guest speaker at the annual general meeting of the Dublin Mathematics Teachers' Association to be held at St Patrick's College, Drumcondra, in Dublin. Speak in front of maths teachers? No way! Why I didn't turn this down I'll never know, but I accepted.

The flight from London to Singapore took thirteen hours. I was very excited to be in such an interesting place and to have a whole day to myself before giving a speech at the closing ceremony. Singapore is, as was explained to me, very much a knowledge-based community, and the government is particularly supportive of the education system. It is very impressive judging from what I saw while there, and the schools I visited were like our third-level institutions in terms of their facilities.

That evening I tried to rehearse a speech I had written for the following day's ceremony. As I tried to block out everything else while pacing the balcony of my 63rd-floor room, Dad delivered frequent but most unhelpful assurances to me that I would be f-i-i-i-i-ne. I wanted to be very familiar with the flow of thought I had worked out and to avoid, as much as possible, reading the script of my speech – a speech which I was now beginning to really dread. What if I messed up after they had flown me all the way from Ireland? To add to the pressure I was scheduled to speak *after* an award winning professor and *before* a very successful researcher.

On the morning of the ceremony the professor began his talk with a light-hearted joke as he moved easily around the stage. I wished he were not so good; every aspect of his speech increased my nervousness and reduced me to a quivering wreck. When his slot was coming to an end and his PowerPoint presentation was about to wrap things up beautifully for him, I, who had only been concentrating on his speech, realised with a shock that I was up next. Yes, here it comes, the master of ceremonies is calling me up on stage after making me out to be the bee's knees.

I reluctantly made my way up the steps and hid behind the nice thick wooden lectern opposite the modern see-through one on the other side of the stage. I unfolded my crumpled pages, cracked my first joke and concentrated on looking first to the left of the room and then to the right, but never to the middle where Dad was sitting. Besides avoiding looking at Dad I was at the same time trying to block out two other rather irritating things – my whole left leg was shaking violently, thankfully in the sanctuary provided by my big blocky lectern, and my face – my quivering white face – was being projected onto two large, two *very* large screens at either side of the stage.

I was concentrating so much on speaking clearly and distinctly that it was only when I slumped into my chair afterwards that I became aware that I had most certainly run over time. Having waited every agonising moment up to my own time to speak, the last thing I would have wished for my audience was that I should spend an eternity speaking to them. I also felt badly about not having made use of a PowerPoint slide presentation, though I had one almost ready. In my few rushed moments that morning I did not have time to make sure it would run smoothly, so rather than have another thing to worry about while standing in front of a very varied audience I easily persuaded myself not to bring it, much to Dad's disappointment. Being so tired I had chosen to ignore his advice and go against even my own instincts. It really would have improved the presentation.

Surprisingly, the part of my speech which everyone picked up on was my discussion of Dad's method of teaching us through puzzles on the blackboard at home. Thankfully this took the attention away from me afterwards, and he was quizzed instead. Later I was chuffed when one of the organisers was able to remember all the main points of my speech in perfect order – even the ones towards the end! When we finally took our leave and went back to the hotel room I was dreading Dad's few words – the inevitable "should have had the PowerPoint" came up, but apart from that the praise was flowing. But I was not accepting any, as I was hung up on the mistakes I had made. I wanted to learn from them, and I wanted to concentrate on the next few days when I would have more opportunities to make amends.

How on earth is everyone so lively here at six in the morning? I was due on the other side of the city by eight thirty for the first of four hour-and-a-half-long talks, now thankfully reduced to three. I had the laptop with my PowerPoint displays this time, and was guarding it dearly on the way to the junior college which was to be my base for the day. These talks were to be more general than the speech at the award ceremony and therefore not so difficult. I had some nice presentations, different ones for different levels of audience. I was still very nervous as I would be talking first to people of my age and then to older students for the remainder of the day. This was rather daunting, especially considering some of the projects I had seen at their science competition. I spoke to each group about why I was there, and how I had got interested in maths and cryptography, and I showed them a few puzzles before taking them in detail through the one on magic squares. I used this to explain that "a little thinking can save a lot of computing", and how by exploring just a bit beyond what you were initially asked you could end up *proving* something (in this case exactly how many magic squares there are). To finish up I went through some of the main ideas of cryptography. There was half an hour allotted at the end of each talk for questions and answers. If this dragged, despite teachers' efforts to get their students to ask more questions, I would throw out a few more challenging puzzles, to which most responded with enthusiasm.

I was exhausted by the time it came to give the last talk that Monday evening, and while waiting to be asked up on stage I nearly fell asleep. However, this talk proved to be the best. Judging from the questions I had been asked after my previous two talks, I now knew which points to explain more fully. I also felt that this time round I had given just the right amount of the personal story. The teachers present were most appreciative of the work I had put in, and it was they who asked the best questions. All in all, I enjoyed the presentations and felt good about having come so well prepared. I talked without notes and so looked at my audience the whole time – a big achievement for me!

I gave one more talk on Tuesday to a more varied group of students at another school. That too went well. I was now free to enjoy the rest of my short stay and experience some of the culture of the East. I visited the Indian and Malayan markets in search of exotic presents, and bought some silk for Mom. In the evenings, Dad and I searched out different restaurants where we experimented with all sorts of oriental dishes, before heading for Boat Quay to sit out in the warm night air drinking beer while soaking up the atmosphere (which, if the truth be told, was more Western than Eastern). There was little fear of ever getting lost on our way back to the hotel, the Westin Stamford, because, being the tallest in the world, it is visible from almost every direction. It was disappointing to be returning home so soon.

After the twenty-three-hour journey home I had exactly seven hours before I was off again on a school tour of Dingle and the mountains of Kerry. I had looked forward to this weekend before ever going to secondary school, and comatose or not I was going to enjoy it. Sometimes the body needs diversion more than it needs sleep. It turned out to be the most fun I had all year. We climbed Mt Brandon and rolled back down in the snow – twice! I laughed so much my stomach hurt. The day after that Mom and I drove to Leenaun in Galway, in order to fit in with the recording schedule of Channel 9, Australia, to do another interview. They were to film in Cork the following day, but by that time I – jet-setter that I had become – would be in Milan for my next engagement.

Despite my experience in Singapore I was never so nervous about anything in my entire life as I was about this presentation in front of two hundred women at the IBM conference. Never! However, my talk (this time with a PowerPoint presentation) was very well received – in fact I was given the only standing ovation of the three-day conference, though I think it might have been out of pity for the seventeen-year-old who had to speak to all those successful career women. I listened with great interest to a number of the other speakers, hearing the kind of things that occupy the minds of business-people – how to improve sales, how to attract a suitable workforce. On this last point one speaker said that the cleverest students, as judged by grade point average, don't necessarily prove to be the best employees – her actual words were,

After-math

"Next to eye colour, grade point average is the most useful indicator of a suitable applicant." They must have liked the colour of my eyes because a week later I was offered a summer job – at any IBM site of my choosing.

I still hadn't learnt my lesson, for near the end of the school year I found myself addressing the Maths Teachers' Association of Dublin. This was quite a turnabout – here was I, standing in front of teachers. But unlike a class of students they had turned up voluntarily. It was to be my biggest challenge yet because I would be addressing a mathematically educated audience who would follow what I said very attentively. I went to a lot of trouble preparing a PowerPoint presentation which included more advanced material, to lend more substance to the talk.

No sooner had I delivered my opening lines than my computer crashed. My confidence must definitely have been increasing because I surprised myself by remaining outwardly calm and rebooting the machine while continuing to talk. Had this happened to me during one of my earlier talks, I would have crashed too! The presentation went smoothly after that, and I could sense that the teachers were quite pleased. With at least one number theorist in the audience that I knew of, it was only to be expected that the questions afterwards would be tough – and they were. They were the best I had been asked in all of my talks.

As I have said, right from the outset Baltimore Technologies were always very careful not to be drawn into saying anything exaggerated about the Cayley–Purser algorithm. In the first few days after my Young Scientist win they couldn't have made any informed comment because they hadn't studied my project report. Although Michael and William had visited the exhibition, they naturally spent most of their time talking with me rather than examining my display in any depth. Baltimore had to be as surprised by the sudden attention they were receiving as I had been when it first came out of the blue at me. Of course, it was my naming of the CP algorithm and my informing the press of the connection that drew all this publicity upon the company. For the first week they, like me, were inundated by journalists looking for a story, so they had little or no time to give attention to my report. However, Michael, because he was so directly involved with it and because he shunned most interviews (leaving them to William, as he was happy to admit), began to think his way back into the ideas. He harboured misgivings that the CP was secure because he had eventually abandoned his own system after finding it not to be entirely to his own satisfaction. Almost a week after that fateful *Times* article, he emailed to say that he recalled an 'attack' on his work which had been pointed out to him by a mathematician and which he felt might also compromise the CP system. An attack on a cryptosystem is something like a prisoner making a Shawshank-type escape from a high-security prison from which escape was believed to be 'impossible'.

When the possibility of an attack on the CP algorithm was first made known to me, I was desperately disappointed. Now that I had been in the public eye so much I couldn't help feeling that I had perpetrated some kind of giant fraud. Deep down, of course, I knew I hadn't done any such thing. I had repeatedly said to reporters that the algorithm was being praised before it had been appraised; that it had not been subjected to the kind of peer review by competent cryptographers that is necessary before any system can be judged to have any merit. Although some did report these cautionary comments, many chose not to. I know most people wouldn't care a straw one way or the other, but for me it was vitally important that people in the mathematical world who had helped me and whom I respected could see that *I* wasn't making any over-the-top claims. I found it very comforting when many mathematicians Dad met afterwards commented on how careful I had been to avoid exaggeration.

Dad and Mom, Michael and William all knew of my discomfort and tried to put me at ease in every possible way. My parents said that it is quite normal in science for one researcher to report an investigation and for another to point out something not quite right or suggest an improvement; that science moves on as much by negative results as by positive ones. A mathematician whose work is found to be less than perfect is still regarded as an active contributor to progress. If things were otherwise, nobody would publish. Michael wrote, "nor is your achievement any less because there is a security problem with the algorithm. There are very few algorithms which stand up to rigorous analysis."

I knew all this was true, but because I had been made out to be such a hot-shot, would the papers suddenly cry "Fraud" if I were to reveal the attack? One newspaper had run an article with the heading NO MILLIONS FOR SARAH. Although it was probably the first hint of a negative note in what so far had been presented as a fairy story, I wasn't upset by it. It was more realistic than most reports up to that time. However, I had no idea that the article was to appear, and it was chilling to realise that reporters could write almost anything they wanted without bothering to check with you on points of fact or how you might feel. One or two articles had been very cavalier about what most would regard as trivial details, such as inventing a description of our kitchen (I'm still looking for the pine table we're supposed to have) and quoting me as saying 'girly' things that I would never say in a million years. So I was uneasy, because I felt that if knowledge of the attack became public prematurely, there was no telling how the press might react. I was also worried for another, more serious reason.

Dad remarked in an email to William that it was ironic that it is the Cayley–Hamilton theorem that undermines the Cayley–Purser algorithm as a public key system. By way of reply, William commented, "Either way, Cayley wins." This humorous observation highlighted something which I hadn't thought about up to now. When dealing with the first burst of publicity I was afraid of drawing attention to people I knew had no interest in receiving it. My gravest concern had been for Michael. By titling my project as I had, to acknowledge how much his ideas had helped me, I had unwittingly brought the attention of the press upon him. I know him to be a man who owns no television set and refuses all TV interviews, so you can imagine how much he values his privacy. (I am conscious that by writing all this I am only further adding to his exposure.) Now the attack was an even greater worry because it might affect how he would be remembered.

In Code

I knew from listening to conversations between scientific friends of my parents how true scientists really despise those who publish any old rubbish to pander to the 'Publish or Perish' maxim. (Dad jokingly said of the attack, "Publish and Perish".) I knew also from correspondence with William and Michael that they were both men who would have no truck with any kind of 'soft science'. They were conscious of their reputations and that of Baltimore's as a serious cryptography company. Even before the attack had reared its head, Michael had written, "We [Baltimore, William and I] could look very foolish, lucky you would be excused on the grounds of youth." Months earlier I had been very much struck by William's saying, "Bad business is one thing, but bad science is another." So I was very conscious now that after a lifetime devoted to mathematics and producing work of the highest quality he might be more thought of as the person connected with 'that faulty algorithm'.

Now that I knew of a possible attack on the CP algorithm, I had first to learn its exact nature. I felt under pressure as people were hoping that I would publish it or post it on a Web site fairly soon. Naturally, Baltimore (through Michael and William) and I wanted some time to try to find what is known as a 'patch'. In stark contrast to those wonderful March and April months when I was full of energy and enthusiasm and had time to investigate, I was now back at school and worn out from either doing interviews in the evenings or being followed around by TV people, while all the time having to deal with letters and emails. As you can imagine, it was very difficult to recover the proper frame of mind necessary to do any kind of work involving clear thinking.

The attack, if it proved to be successful, essentially meant that the CP algorithm could no longer be classified as a public key system, which was its main claim to fame, though it could still be regarded as a valid cryptosystem. But it held little attraction for me unless it could be restored to its original status.

I took a long time to settle back to work. Despite exploring different variations which held out promise, my feelings of hope were always short-lived. I was to learn a good deal more mathematics but unfortunately I was also to learn in the end that the algorithm couldn't be patched. Its public element simply gives just a little too much information to the bad guys.

Whereas Baltimore had been anxious to publish something a month or so after the storm of publicity first blew up, I asked that we not do this until I had attended the European Contest in September. Besides wanting to stay quiet about the attack for a while longer, I didn't want the status of the project as Ireland's entry to be compromised by any discussions that might arise on the Internet.

Throughout this whole period Dad, Michael and William snatched whatever time they could to think about and discuss the attack with me, as did one very renowned mathematician. On reading my report he immediately saw where the CP system was vulnerable, but thought it a matter of little consequence in the grand scheme of things. I was really cheered by his attitude. His whole outlook was completely positive. He viewed the publicity for the Young Scientist '99 winning project as a great advertisement for mathematics, and he hoped my win would help lift the image of his beloved discipline and attract back the bright young minds which for the moment are being lost to the other sciences. What a lift I got on hearing this. That I might have done a service to someone or something, never mind its exact nature, made me feel good, even proud.

As soon as I finished school I got cracking on my forms and report which had to be submitted by 1 June to the EU Contest judges. The forms were easy – they just wanted straightforward facts. The worst part was the scaling down of the project report. The one I had written for Dublin was in the region of 50 pages long, but now "the written project may consist of up to a maximum of 10 pages of written text. It may be accompanied by up to a further 10 pages of illustrations." Ouch!

What a lot of tedious work and tough decisions – what should go and what should stay? The most difficult part emotionally was writing a postscript detailing the nature of the attack on the CP algorithm. In accordance with this 'addition', I called the project for the EU Young Scientist competition, 'Cryptography: An

Investigation of a New Algorithm Versus the RSA'. In true Irish style I sent off the forms and report by courier on the morning of 1 June!

Beginning the second week of July, I spent four weeks at the Smart Card Division in IBM Development Laboratories, Böblingen, near Stuttgart in Germany. While I was apprehensive about what their expectations of me might be, I quickly settled into my new workplace with the support primarily of my "foster parents", Elke and Stefan. They work in the division and were exceptionally kind to me, taking me to classical music concerts in the magnificent castles of the region and, best of all, taking me hiking in the Swiss and Austrian Alps. A highlight of my stay was a visit to the IBM Research Laboratory in Zurich, Switzerland, where I was really impressed by the exciting and unpressurised atmosphere of innovation. There is little or no hierarchy in the workforce, just Dr This and Dr That. Each researcher appeared to be working on something unique on the cutting edge and – most importantly, as far as I'm concerned – investigating a problem of his or her own choosing. What's more, they all seemed to have good, well-paid jobs. I could work in a place like that!

The first day of September saw me in my final school year and signing the contract for this book. What a start to a month. Two weeks later Mom and the boys flew to Greece, and I went with Dad and a friend of his to Dublin for the All-Ireland Hurling Final (which Cork won – UP THE REBELS!). The day after, in high spirits, I paid a visit to Baltimore, where I spoke with William about the posting of the project on their Web pages once I had made it public in Greece. Then it was back home for a week of sustained hard work. I went through every detail over and over again, particularly the postscript, because I imagined this would be where the European judges would focus most of their attention. Dad and I ate in Chinese restaurants for the entire week (he always takes up this lifestyle when Mom goes away with the younger boys), and I watched videos at night utterly wrecked after each day's work. I had to pass up a wonderful invitation from the Irish Computer Society to spend a week at a conference in Bunratty Castle where I could have met Whitfield Diffie, one of the founding fathers of public key cryptography. That was very disappointing, but it would simply have been too much so close to the competition.

Ευρωπαικος Διαγωνισμος για Νεους Επιστημονες

Although I got no chance to let the sun change the shade of my skin during the week in Thessaloniki, Greece, I made a lot of friends and enjoyed the magnificent food and cultural events our Greek hosts had laid on for us. All the participants got on really well together, and my gang of friends told jokes all week despite the sweltering heat of the exhibition hall – the only thing that wasn't excellent, but only because the air conditioning wasn't working.

The atmosphere at the exhibition was very relaxed, partly because, I think, the judges had been able to study the project reports since June. Each report had already been given a preliminary mark, which meant that the judging process wasn't as intense as I had found it to be in Dublin. As in all competitions I have been to, there was a great variation in the standard of presentation and in content. When it came to displays, some entrants seemed to be clueless while others had their posters made professionally and had made flyers describing their projects. This contrast in standard was probably due to the fact that each country's national contest is organised differently, some placing more emphasis on visual presentation than others.

My main judge, a mathematician, commended me on the integrity I had shown by including a detailed report on the attack. Phew! He wished to know if I was disappointed about the demise of the algorithm as a public key system. He was also very interested in hearing about the visits I had made to Singapore and Milan, because he devotes much of his time to popularising mathematics.

In all I was visited by eleven of the fourteen judges. Some had shown my project report to cryptographer acquaintances, who, they informed me, had been very enthusiastic about it. The more mathematically knowledgeable judges asked great general questions about this and that cryptographic matter with a "What did I think of this?" and "Wasn't this cool?" All in all I was pleased with my performance and heartened by the number of interviews I received.

The award ceremony was held in one of the summer residences of the former King of Greece under a magnificent sunset reflected in the Aegean Sea. There was a big build-up to the main prizes. The three third-prize winners were all announced before a more detailed description was given about each of the three projects that had won second prizes. When a French girl, whose stand was near mine, got one of these for her project on volcanoes, I thought I no longer had a chance as she'd had more judging interviews than I had. Dad, on the other hand, was confident that I was among the winners because after the second prizes had been announced he had noticed that we were being photographed: he knew that 'there was something cooking in the pot'. I didn't think so. Because of the attack I was really prepared to go home empty-handed but proud that I had done my best. I was astounded when my name was called out first as one of the first-prize winners. As I walked up the grand steps to a huge cheer from all my new friends, I was delighted. My beloved CP algorithm may not have turned out to be earth-shatteringly amazing, but it was still good science.

Moments later I was sent into an emotional spin when the president of the jury made me stay on the stage. He wished to present me with another prize, one of the Honorary Awards. It was a week-long trip to Stockholm in December to attend the Nobel Prize ceremonies. I couldn't believe it. I shall regard this visit as the perfect end to what has been an eventful year.

I got a celebrity welcome-home. On my arrival at Cork Airport I was met by photographers and whisked into the VIP lounge. My achievements were hailed as a great victory for Cork and an antidote to Cork's loss in the All-Ireland Football Final just minutes after the plane had landed. The first radio interview I did was with Morning Ireland – a news programme broadcast nationwide between 7.30 and 9.00. In this interview with me and 'the proud parents', we commented on the attack so as to kill off all the stories about the algorithm making billions and my being a genius. With a huge weight off my shoulders, I was free at last to do what I had always wanted to do. I sent a copy of the project, warts and all, to Ron Rivest.*

I was never really sure (and I'm still not) about what I'd like to be 'when I grow up'. Until recently I had no definite ideas on what to study at university, other than some vague notion that it would be something in the sciences. I suppose I have been a little anxious not to be seen to follow in Dad's footsteps. However, over this last year I have decided that, to start with at least, I'd like to study maths and computer science. In this way I'll learn more about cryptography, which I feel will always hold a very strong attraction for me. I hope to stay at university long enough to earn a Ph.D. I trust that, in addition to being productive, my college years will be lots of fun. Ultimately I would like to be one of those lucky people who get paid for doing what they love.

---

* Because of its technical nature I have not included a description of it in this book. Those who are interested can find it at the Web site www.cayley-purser.ie.

About This Book

Writing this book was torture. We could never have done it without Mom's help. She was our primary proofreader, earning herself the name Mme Fowler for her readiness to cite *Modern English Usage* in defence of her proposed alterations. Later, her job description broadened to include monitoring the mathematics sections for what she termed 'breaches of promise' – a reference to the aim stated near the beginning of the book that the mathematics should be intelligible to all readers. Of course, very early on we all realised that her usefulness in this role was becoming diminished, as with each reading to check for improvements her understanding of the material deepened. This led to Dad changing her title to 'Gorenstein's chauffeur'.

The story goes that, in the course of a long lecture tour, the famous American mathematician Daniel Gorenstein was chauffeur driven to various venues around the USA. While Gorenstein lectured, his chauffeur sat in the back row of the auditorium. In time the chauffeur became so familiar with the material (and it was pretty deep stuff) that he joked to Gorenstein, "At this stage, I reckon I could give that lecture myself". One evening, Gorenstein was scheduled to speak at a small university where he guessed his face wouldn't be known. Feeling particularly tired, the master hit upon the idea of asking the chauffeur to give the lecture while he would rest in the back row. The lecture went off without a hitch, and at the end the chauffeur answered without hesitation all the questions, which he had heard asked and answered a hundred times before; all, that is, except for one last question which left him entirely at a loss. After a momentary panic, he composed himself and said, "That question is so simple, I believe even my chauffeur could answer it." The dozing 'chauffeur' shamed the questioner with an immediate reply.

Mom's final contribution was the following: "Don't worry, Sarah. If people like this book, you'll get all the credit, but if they don't, Dad will get all the blame!"

Appendix A
Solutions to Puzzles

Two Jars: Fill up the five litre jar. Then use it to fill the three litre jar so that two litres remain in the five litre jar. Empty the three litre jar and pour the two litres from the five litre jar into the three litre jar. Fill up the five litre jar again and use it to top up the three litre jar with the extra litre it needs. Four litres now remain in the five litre jar.

Alternatively fill up the three litre jar and pour its contents into the five litre jar. Fill up the three litre jar again and use it to top up the five litre jar with the extra two litres it needs. Now empty the five litre jar, and pour the litre that is in the three litre jar into the empty five litre jar. Fill up the three litre jar again and pour its contents into the five litre jar. The five litre jar now contains exactly four litres.

My youngest brother Eamonn says, "Start filling and pouring and just keep going." He's right. You will eventually end up with what you were asked to get, provided it's possible. With a nine litre jar and a six litre jar you *cannot* measure five litres exactly. On the other hand, with a nine litre jar and a seven litre jar it is possible to measure out exactly every measure from one to nine litres. This is because the numbers 7 and 9 are *relatively prime* to each other.

A variation on this Two Jars puzzle is the Egg-Timer puzzle. How would you boil a four minute egg with two egg-timers which measure three and five minutes respectively, and what is the shortest

Appendix A – Solutions to Puzzles

amount of time required? You'll have to answer this one for yourself.

Rabbit: Because the rabbit goes up three metres every day and then slides back down two, she gains a metre every day. However, it would be an error to conclude that she escapes from the well after 30 days. The manner in which she gains the metre per day is all-important. After 27 days she is three metres from the top. On the 28th day she reaches the top and runs off. It takes the rabbit only 28 days to get out of the well.

One Hundred Metre Race: When A crosses the 100 metre line to win, B is at the 90 metre mark because he covers 9 metres for every 10 metres that A does. Similarly, since B beats C by 10 metres, C covers only 9 metres for every 10 metres that B does, so when B has covered 90 metres, C has covered only nine-tenths of 90 metres, which is 81 metres. So when A crosses the 100 metre line to win, C is at the 81 metre mark. Thus A beats C by 19 metres.

Russian Postal System: Boris in Moscow rings Natasha in St Petersburg and tells her that he will place the gem in the strongbox, lock it with a padlock and post it to her. Because it is locked it will arrive safely in St Petersburg. She is then to lock the strongbox a second time with a padlock of her own and post it back to him in Moscow. He will then remove his lock and send the strongbox, with the gem still safely locked inside, back to her again. This time when it arrives safely in St Petersburg she can open it. Neat!

Twenty People at a Party: Imagine each of the people at the party wearing a T-shirt with a number written on the front of it. This number tells how many people at the party this person knows. So the guy with the number 4 on his shirt knows exactly four people (outside of knowing himself, which doesn't count). Someone else with the number 11 knows exactly eleven people at the party. Since the *largest* number of people any one person can know is nineteen (all the others), the largest possible number that can be seen on any T-shirt is 19. Similarly, since the *smallest* number of people any one person can know is zero (none of the others), the smallest possible number that can be seen on a T-shirt is 0.

However, if there is someone in the room with the number 19 on his shirt (meaning that this person knows everybody else), then there *cannot* be a person in the room with the number 0 on his shirt. And, if there is someone in the room with the number 0 on his shirt (meaning that this person knows nobody else) then there *cannot* be a person in the room with the number 19 on his shirt. This is the key observation. In either case, there are only nineteen different numbers that can appear on T-shirts, either those ranging from 1 to 19 or those ranging from 0 to 18. Since there are twenty people in the room, some two people must have the same number on their shirts and so know the same number of people.

Appendix B
Answers to Miscellaneous
Questions

Early Influences

Page 19: *If so, the cell marked with a * must contain the number 1 (why?).*

Because 9,5 and * must sum to 15.

Page 20: *The numbers A and B in the first column cannot be any of 6,7 or 8 (why?).*

Because each, when added to the 9 in the central side cell, give a sum of at least 15 with just two numbers.

Mathematical Excursions

Page 30: *Can you find the number less than 1000 which has the most factors?*

I suppose only you can answer this question with a 'yes' or a 'no'.

However, the number is 840, which has 32 factors. The number 720 has 30 factors, while the number 960 has 28 factors.

Page 32: *Are there other rectangular arrangements (of the number 889364)?*

Yes. Here are all the possible rectangular arrangements, beginning with the trivial one:

$$
\begin{aligned}
1 &\times 889364 \\
2 &\times 444682 \\
4 &\times 222341 \\
7 &\times 127052 \\
14 &\times 63526 \\
23 &\times 38668 \\
28 &\times 31763 \\
46 &\times 19334 \\
92 &\times 9667 \\
161 &\times 5524 \\
322 &\times 2762 \\
644 &\times 1381
\end{aligned}
$$

Page 41: *Do you now see why the first 120 numbers were chosen to demonstrate this remarkably simple algorithm?*

Again, only you can answer this question with a 'yes' or a 'no'. However, the first 120 numbers were chosen because sievings based on the four primes 2,3,5 and 7 sieve out *all* the composites less than or equal to 120, but do not sieve out the composite 121. This requires a sieving based on the fifth prime, 11, because $121 = 11 \times 11$.

Page 43: *Prove that there are at least two people in Dublin with the same numbers of hairs on their heads.*

Try to imagine a big head, and make a rough estimate of the

Appendix B – Answers to Misc. Questions

number of hairs that could be on that head. I suppose 2 per mm^2 is a bit light: let's overestimate it at an enormous 10 per mm^2, which is 1000 per cm^2. This is pretty hairy.

Now for the size of this head: suppose it's a sphere with about half its surface area covered with hair. The area of a hemisphere of radius R is $2\pi R^2$. What would R be for a bighead? Well, my basketball has a diameter of 23.25 cm. Let's suppose a bighead's diameter to be a whopping 30 cm, so its radius R would be 15 cm. So the hairy bighead area is

$$2 \times \pi \times 15^2 \approx 1414$$

rounding up to 1450 cm^2. How many hairs sprout from 1450cm^2 if there are 1000 per cm^2? Answer:

$$1450 \times 1000 = 1450000$$

I hope you will agree that this is an absolute maximum.

Now, how many people live in Dublin? I'm told at least 1500000. Let's settle for that. Suppose now that a survey is done on the number of hairs on the head of each Dubliner. Suppose also that by some miracle each of the first 1450001 people surveyed has a different number of hairs. Now all the possible hair-numbers which lie between 0 and 1450001 have been used. Any one of the remaining 49999 citizens also has a hair-number which lies between 0 and 1450001 and so matches the hair-number of one of the persons in the first 1450001 people surveyed. So there *must* be at least two people with the same number of hairs on their heads.

Page 48: *Check that M(10) = 2^{10} − 1 = 1023 is indeed composite.*

The digits of the number 1023 add to 6. Since this is divisible by 3, then so is the number 1023. Dividing 1023 by 3 gives 341. Since 341 = 11 × 31, the complete factorisation of 1023 is 3 × 11 × 31.

241

In Code

Page 49: *The number $2^{11} - 1 = 2047$ is not a prime.*

Its smallest prime factor is 23 and its remaining prime factor is 89. Observe that $23 = 2 \times 11 + 1$ and $89 = 8 \times 11 + 1$. Curious?

What Matters Is What's Left Over

Page 69: *Decipher* **wubdjdlq**, *assuming it has been enciphered using a 3-shift.*

Answer: **tryagain**, taken as "try again".

Occasionally a word becomes another recognisable English word when it is enciphered.

The word 'cold' enciphers to 'frog' under a 3-shift.

What happens to 'pecan' in a 4-shift cipher?

The word 'pecan' enciphers to 'tiger' under a 4-shift.

What happen to 'sleep' in a 9-shift cipher?

The word 'sleep' enciphers to 'bunny' under a 9-shift.

Page 83: *Things are much worse when every P-number is multiplied by 13 modulo 26. Do a few multiplications and see.*

The following array shows the results of enciphering the numbers 0 to 25 according to the rule $C = 13P \bmod 26$:

Appendix B – Answers to Misc. Questions

P	→	C		P	→	C
0	→	0		13	→	13
1	→	13		14	→	0
2	→	0		15	→	13
3	→	13		16	→	0
4	→	0		17	→	13
5	→	13		18	→	0
6	→	0		19	→	13
7	→	13		20	→	0
8	→	0		21	→	13
9	→	13		22	→	0
10	→	0		23	→	13
11	→	13		24	→	0
12	→	0		25	→	13

When you have found the inverse of 7 modulo 26, try to find the inverse of 4 modulo 26.

The inverse of 7 modulo 26 is 15, because $15 \times 7 = 105$ and $105 \bmod 26 = 1$. The number 4 has no inverse modulo 26. There is no whole number between 0 and 25 which, when multiplied by 4 and reduced modulo 26, yields 1. Just look at the array showing the results of enciphering the numbers 0 to 25 according to the rule $C = 4P \bmod 26$.

Page 88: *Then the P-number assigned to* go *is*

$$P = (6 \times 26) + 14 = 170$$

Can you explain why this is correct?

Once again, only you can answer this question with a 'yes' or a 'no'. However, the group of digraphs with leading character g, beginning ga, gb, gc and ending gx, gy, gz, is the *seventh* group, because g is the seventh character of the lowercase alphabet. The first six groups contain $6 \times 26 = 156$ digraphs, which are labelled with the numbers

0 to 155. Since o is the fifteenth character of the lower-case alphabet, the digraph go is the fifteenth in its group and so has the number $155 + 15 = 170$.

Sums with a Difference

Page 106: *If the number 675 represents a Wednesday, which day of the week does the number 943 represent?*

Since $943 - 675 = 268 = 38 \times 7 + 2$, the number 943 represents a Friday because it is 38 weeks and 2 days after the Wednesday represented by the number 675. The alert reader will have noticed that this question is posed in a slightly different form – and answered – a few paragraphs previously.

Page 116: *Then add this 8 to 6 to get 5. (Why?)*

Because $8 + 6 = 14$ and $14 \bmod 9 = 5$, as $14 = 1 \times 9 + 5$.

Page 127: *Can you find two non-trivial factors of 11111?*

Again, over to you for a 'yes' or a 'no'. However, 41×271 is the complete factorisation of 11111.

Page 135: *Should you switch?*

Yes. In order to think clearly about the problem get someone to help you simulate the game show with three mugs (to act as the doors) and a matchstick (to act as the car). Close your eyes and get your helper to hide the matchstick under one of the mugs at random. Then open your eyes, choose a mug and let your helper reveal a mug with nothing under it. Play this game many times, and count how often you win by not switching and how often by switching.

The following explanation of the answer "Yes, you should switch" is due to Erich Neuwirth of Bad Voeslau, Austria, and appears on page 369 of the Mathematical Association of America's *The College Mathematics Journal*, Vol. 30, No. 5, November 1999:

> Imagine two players, the first one always staying with the selected door and the second one always switching. Then, in each game, exactly one of them wins. Since the winning probability for the strategy 'Don't switch' is $\frac{1}{3}$, the winning probability for the second one is $\frac{2}{3}$ and therefore switching is the way to go.

One Way Only

Page 140: Can you find p and q?

No!

Do you want to ?

Probably not.

P a g e   1 4 3 : *What would you say about the oddness or otherwise of x if you were to receive a y that is even?*

That x is even because (in ordinary arithmetic) an odd number cubed is always an odd number.

P a g e   1 4 9 : *For ten people, 45 such meetings are needed. Why?*

Imagine each of the ten people shaking hands. Each person would shake the hand of each of the other nine. Since there are two people involved in each handshake, the total number of handshakes is 45 as this number is one-half of $10 \times 9 = 90$.

P a g e   1 6 3 : *You might like to help Alice, Bob and Clare to figure out what to do if they wish Denis to join their team and still maintain* *a threshold of two, meaning that any two of the team of four can work without the others being present. In other words, they need you to help them come up with a (2, 4) scheme. Will they have to buy more locks, or can they get away with making more keys to the locks they already have?*

Yes and no. They will have to buy one more lock. They cannot get away with just making more keys to the three locks they already have. The reason is simple. Because they require a (2, 4) scheme it must be that each one of them is unable to open (at least) one lock. If there are only three locks, then since there are four people some two of them, say Alice and Bob, cannot open the *same* lock, L_1 (lock one) for example. However, this means that there is one group of two people unable to work, namely Alice and Bob, whereas the intention is that *any* group of two can open the cabinet to begin work. Hence at least four locks are needed with each member of the group unable to open a lock different from the ones the other members are unable to open. In fact, four locks will do if each member is given three keys according to the following scheme (the four locks are labelled L_1, L_2, L_3 and L_4 respectively):

Alice has a key for each of L_1, L_2, L_3 but not for L_4
Bob has a key for each of L_1, L_2, L_4 but not for L_3
Clare has a key for each of L_1, L_3, L_4 but not for L_2
Denis has a key for each of L_1, L_3, L_4 but not for L_1

It is clear that for any two people, each has the key the other is missing.

Appendix C
Euclid's Algorithm

The greatest common divisor (g.c.d.) of any two natural numbers is the largest natural number that divides each of them.

In general, the notation (c, d) stands for, and is read as, the greatest common divisor of the numbers c and d. For example, $(8, 12) = 4$ says that the greatest common divisor of 8 and 12 is 4, while $(30, 78) = 6$ says that the greatest common divisor of 30 and 78 is 6. On the other hand, $(10, 21) = 1$ because 10 and 21 have no factor in common other than 1. The numbers 10 and 21 are *relatively prime* to each other.

Surprisingly, $(m, 0) = m$ for any natural number m. Why? Because every m is a factor of 0 since $0 = 0 \times m$. Thus, for example, $(30, 0) = 30$, while $(11, 0) = 11$.

But a nice notation is not enough to tell us how to find the g.c.d. of two numbers. For example, what is $(4950, 420)$? In words, what is the g.c.d. of the two numbers 4950 and 420?

Because both numbers end in 0, you might say that – at the very least – they have the factor 10 in common. Having made this observation (which won't always be valid), you might examine the numbers 495 and 42 to see which factors they have in common. After a little thought, it might occur to you to find the complete factorisation of both of the original numbers, pick out those factors in common and form their product to get the desired greatest common divisor.

In Code

Since

$$4950 = 2 \times 3^2 \times 5^2 \times 11$$
$$420 = 2^2 \times 3 \times 5 \times 7$$

the two numbers share the factors 2, 3 and 5. Since $2 \times 3 \times 5 = 30$, it must be that

$$(4950, 420) = 30$$

That wasn't too difficult. But fundamentally, as an approach, it is very seriously flawed because it requires the complete factorisation, of the two numbers whose g.c.d. is sought. Since factorisation is believed, with some justification, to be a tremendously difficult problem in general, this method cannot be considered a useful one. To convince yourself on this point, write down two random 100-digit numbers and try to find their g.c.d.

Euclid's algorithm

Now for a bit of good news. Over two thousand years ago, Euclid described a very efficient method for finding the g.c.d. of any two natural numbers, which *does not require* knowledge of their factorisations. The method is based on a simple general observation which can be illustrated using the two 'smallish' numbers 4920 and 420. The observation is

$$(4950, 420) = (420, 4950 \bmod 420)$$

Let us unpack this a little to see what is being said. Since

$$4950 = 11 \times 420 + 330 \Rightarrow 4950 \bmod 420 = 330$$

the observation simplifies to

Appendix C - Euclid's Algorithm

$$(4950, 420) = (420, 330)$$

What is this all-important fact, which I'm asking you to take on trust as being true, saying? It says that the g.c.d. of the original pair of numbers {4950, 420} is *exactly the same* as the g.c.d. of the pair of numbers {420, 330}. This is a very big deal. Why? Because the second pair of numbers is much friendlier than the first pair – the new number 330 in the second pair is smaller that the first number 4950 of the original pair. It should be easier to find (420, 330) rather than (4950, 420).

Now for a brilliant stroke. The original observation applied to (420, 330) says that

$$(420, 330) = (330, 420 \bmod 330)$$

or that

$$(420, 330) = (330, 90)$$

since $420 = 1 \times 330 = 90$ gives $420 \bmod 330 = 90$. Hence

$$(4950, 420) = (420, 330) = (330, 90)$$

Common sense suggests that we do exactly to (330, 90) what has already been done to (4950, 420) and (420, 330). Another such 'iteration' gives

$$(4950, 420) = (420, 330) = (330, 90) = (90, 60)$$

since $330 = 3 \times 90 + 60 \Rightarrow 330 \bmod 90 = 60$. It is possible to stop now, since (90, 60) = 30 by inspection, and conclude that (4950, 420) = 30. This is the same answer as we obtained previously.

Streamlining all the calculation required in the above procedure (and doing two more) gives

$$4950 = 11 \times 420 + 330$$
$$420 = 1 \times 330 + 90$$
$$330 = 3 \times 90 + 60$$
$$90 = 1 \times 60 + 30$$
$$60 = 2 \times 30 + 0$$

from which the series of equalities

$$(4950, 420) = (420, 330) = (330, 90) = (90, 60) = (60, 30) = (30, 0)$$

follow. Since $(30, 0) = 30$, the g.c.d. of the numbers 4950 and 420 is 30.

The reason for carrying the calculations as far as we have is that a program implementing the procedure stops when it encounters the remainder 0 in the last line. The last non-zero remainder appearing in the previous line is the desired g.c.d. of the two numbers.

This magnificently simple and efficient procedure, which uses nothing but basic arithmetic, has been known for centuries as *Euclid's algorithm* or the *Euclidean algorithm*. With very slight modifications it is still the algorithm used by today's 'number crunchers' to find the greatest common divisor of two numbers. This algorithm always terminates because the number of possible remainders is at most the size of the smaller of the two numbers whose g.c.d. is sought.

Euclid's algorithm can be used to find the multiplicative inverse of a number with respect to a modulus (whenever the number possesses such an inverse). The fact that the algorithm does this very efficiently is of some importance. In Chapter 3, 'What Matters Is What's Left Over', the multiplicative inverse of 5 modulo 26 was needed in order to obtain the deciphering rule corresponding to the enciphering rule $C = 5P \bmod 26$. This inverse is obtained by first using Euclid's algorithm to determine $(26, 5)$, even though it is obvious without calculation that the answer is 1. Imitating the procedure discussed above, the following array of calculations is obtained:

$$26 = 5 \times 5 + 1$$
$$5 = 5 \times 1 + 0$$

Appendix C – Euclid's Algorithm

Since the last non-vanishing remainder is 1, it's the case that $(26, 5)$ = 1. Having determined that $(26, 5)$ = 1, we begin a second procedure of writing the g.c.d. 1 in terms of 26 and 5. When this is done, we'll explain why it is a useful thing to do. The first line of the array

$$26 = 5 \times 5 + 1$$

can be rearranged to give

$$1 \times 26 + (-5) \times 5 = 1$$

This last equation shows that 1 can be written as a combination of 26 and 5. Specifically, it shows that 1 can be made by combining one 26 with minus five 5's. Writing the equation as

$$(-5) \times 5 = -1 \times 26 + 1$$

gives

$$(-5 \times 5) \bmod 26 = 1$$

This is very significant. It says that when the number 5 is multiplied by -5 and the result reduced modulo 26, the number 1 is obtained. So -5 is a multiplicative inverse of 5 modulo 26. Because -5 is not in the range 0 to 25, it is not regarded as *the* multiplicative inverse of 5 modulo 26. However, since $-5 \bmod 26$ = 21, the multiplicative inverse of 5 modulo 26, is taken to be 21. It is easy to confirm that 21 is a multiplicative inverse of 5 modulo 26, as follows:

$$21 \times 5 = 105 = 4 \times 26 + 1 \Rightarrow (21 \times 5) \bmod 26 = 1$$

Thus has Euclid's algorithm been used to find the multiplicative inverse of 5 modulo 26. Hence the deciphering rule corresponding to the enciphering rule $C = 5P \bmod 26$ is

In Code

$$P = 21C \bmod 26$$

Knowing that 21 is the muliplicative inverse of 5 allows us (by glossing over some details) to sketch an explanation of why

$$P = (21C + 12) \bmod 26$$

is the deciphering rule corresponding to the enciphering rule

$$C = (5P + 18) \bmod 26$$

Adding -18 to both sides of this equation gives

$$(C - 18) = 5P \bmod 26$$

or

$$5P = (C + 8) \bmod 26$$

since $-18 \bmod 26 = 8$. Multiplying both sides of this equation by 21, which is the multiplicative inverse of 5, and reducing 105 modulo 26 to 1 gives

$$P = 21\,(C + 8) \bmod 26$$

Since $21 \times 8 = 168 = 6 \times 26 + 12$, the above can be written as

$$P = (21C + 12) \bmod 26$$

This, then, is the deciphering rule corresponding to the enciphering rule

$$C = (5P + 18) \bmod 26$$

Appendix C – Euclid's Algorithm

Finding Multiplicative Inverses

The calculations involved in finding the multiplicative inverse of 5 modulo 26 are a little too short to reveal the full extent of what must often be done to determine the multiplicative inverse of a number. Greater insight into the method is gained by using it to compute the multiplicative inverse of 7 modulo 26. The following array of calculations

$$26 = 3 \times 7 + 5$$
$$7 = 1 \times 5 + 2$$
$$5 = 2 \times 2 + 1$$
$$2 = 2 \times 1 + 0$$

shows that $(26, 7) = 1$.

We now begin the second stage of the procedure for finding the multiplicative inverse of 7 modulo 26. This requires that we 'work back up the array' so as to express 1 as a combination of 26 and 7. Beginning with the next-to-last line in the array (which has the remainder 1), we rearrange it to read

$$1 = 5 - 2 \times 2$$

This result, which is obviously true, shows 1 written as a combination of 5 and 2. Now, using the previous line with the remainder 2 written in the form $2 = 7 - 1 \times 5$, we substitute for 2 in the above equation and get

$$1 = 5 - 2 \times (7 - 1 \times 5) \quad \text{or} \quad 1 = 3 \times 5 - 2 \times 7$$

This result, which is obviously true, now shows 1 written as a combination of 7 and 5. Finally, the first line of the array of calculations says that $5 = 26 - (3 \times 7)$, so substituting for 5 in the last equation displayed gives

$$1 = 3 \times (26 - 3 \times 7) - 2 \times 7$$

In Code

Tidying up this expression gives

$$1 = 3 \times 26 - 11 \times 7$$

another result which is easy to verify.

By working back up the array in the manner just outlined, we are able to express the g.c.d. of 26 and 7, which is 1, as a combination of 26 and 7. It is the presence of the 26 in $1 = 3 \times 26 - 11 \times 7$ which is all important. It allows us to say that

$$-11 \times 7 = -3 \times 26 + 1$$

or equivalently that

$$(-11 \times 7) \bmod 26 = 1$$

This says that when the number 7 is multiplied by -11 and the result reduced modulo 26, the number 1 is obtained. Thus -11 is a mulitplicative inverse of 7 modulo 26. Since $-11 \bmod 26 = 15$, the multiplicative inverse of 7 modulo 26 is 15.

$$15 \times 7 = 105 = 4 \times 26 + 1$$

shows that

$$(15 \times 7) \bmod 26 = 1$$

This method of finding the multiplicative inverse of a number modulo another number may strike you as a form of black magic. Even if it doesn't, you will almost certainly think that it is laborious or tedious because you must first calculate the array in the forward direction and, when this is done, you must work your way back up through it to write the number 1 as a combination of the original two numbers. For a human being all this may indeed be tiresome, but for a properly programmed computer it is not. There is a modern version of Euclid's algorithm, called the extended Euclidean algorithm

Appendix C – Euclid's Algorithm

which allows both the forward process and the backward process to be done simultaneously – or in 'one pass', to use modern jargon. This is fantastic as it gives the g.c.d. and expresses it as a linear combination of the two numbers.

I show (without explanation, sorry!) the relevant array of calculations when this extended algorithm is applied to the numbers 26 and 7, in the hope that you might be curious and look up a textbook to learn what on earth is going on. Here it is:

1	0	26	–
0	1	7	–
1	–3	5	3
–1	4	2	1
3	–11	1	2
–	–	0	2

Mysteriously, the second-to-last row reveals that $(26,7) = 1$ and that

$$3 \times 26 + (-11) \times 7 = 1$$

The extended Euclidean algorithm applied to the numbers 676 and 159 yields the array

1	0	676	–
0	1	159	–
1	–4	40	4
–3	13	39	3
4	–17	1	1
–	–	0	39

In Code

The second-to-last row reveals that $(676, 159) = 1$ and that

$$4 \times 676 + (-17) \times 159 = 1$$

Should you require the multiplicative inverse of 159 modulo 676 then this equation leads you to it almost immediately. Rewriting the equation as

$$(-17) \times 159 = -4 \times 676 + 1$$

shows that -17 is a multiplicative inverse of 159 modulo 676. Since $-17 \bmod 676 = 659$, the multiplicative inverse of 159 modulo 676 is 659.

Knowing that 659 is the multiplicative inverse of 159 modulo 676 allows the deciphering rule corresponding to the enciphering rule

$$C = (159P + 580) \bmod 676$$

to be calculated. Adding -580 to both sides of this equation gives

$$(C - 580) = 159P \bmod 676$$

or

$$159P = (C + 96) \bmod 26$$

since $-580 \bmod 676 = 96$. Multiplying both sides of this equation by 659 (which is the multiplicative inverse of 159), and reducing all products modulo 676, gives

$$P = (659C + 396) \bmod 676$$

since $659 \times 96 = 57992 = 93 \times 676 + 396$. Thus

$$P = (659C + 396) \bmod 676$$

is the deciphering rule corresponding to the enciphering rule

$$C = (159P + 580) \bmod 676$$

Appendix D

The Euler ϕ-function and the Euler–Fermat Theorem

Leonhard Euler wrote $\phi(n)$ for the number of positive integers less than a positive integer n which are relatively prime to n. Two natural numbers are *relatively prime* to each other if 1 is the only factor they have in common. For example, $\phi(12) = 4$ since only the four integers 1, 5, 7 and 11 in the set $\{1, 2, 3, 4, 5, 6, 7, 8, 9, 10, 11\}$ of positive integers less than 12 are relatively prime to 12.

Can you make any observations about the function $\phi(n)$ by examining the following table ?

Values of $\phi(n)$ for n = 2 to 32

n	$\phi(n)$	n	$\phi(n)$	n	$\phi(n)$	n	$\phi(n)$	n	$\phi(n)$
2	1	8	4	14	6	21	12	27	18
3	2	9	6	15	8	22	10	28	12
4	2	10	4	16	8	23	22	29	28
5	4	11	10	17	16	24	8	30	8
6	2	12	4	18	6	25	20	31	30
7	6	13	12	19	18	26	12	32	16

Here are some values of $\phi(n)$ when n is a prime number:

$$\phi(7) = 6 \quad \phi(13) = 12 \quad \phi(31) = 30$$

257

In Code

Check some more prime values. Hopefully, your observations will lead you to conjecture that

$$\phi(p) = p - 1$$

whenever p is a prime. This is true in general, since the $p - 1$ positive integers *less* than a prime number p can only have the factor 1 in common with p.

This is a very important rule. When combined with two others which are less obvious, $\phi(n)$ can be calculated for any natural number n *provided* the complete factorisation of the number n is known. Before I tell you about these rules, let me show you something. Observe that

$$4 = \phi(12) = \phi(3) \times \phi(4) = 2 \times 2$$

but that

$$4 = \phi(12) \neq \phi(2) \times \phi(6) = 1 \times 2$$

Furthermore,

$$6 = \phi(18) = \phi(2) \times \phi(9) = 1 \times 6$$

but

$$6 = \phi(18) \neq \phi(3) \times \phi(6) = 2 \times 2$$

It would appear that if $n = r \times s$ then $\phi(n) = \phi(r) \times \phi(s)$ sometimes, but not always. Here is the secret about the property the factors r and s must possess:

$$\phi(n) = \phi(r \times s) = \phi(r) \times \phi(s) \quad \text{whenever} \quad (r, s) = 1$$

This is a very important rule, which is not so easy to prove.

The remaining important rule – which is much easier to prove –

Appendix D – The Euler φ-function

is that

$$\phi(p^k) = p^k - p^{k-1}$$

when p is a prime and k is any positive integer. For example, this rule says that

$$\phi(32) = \phi(2^5) = 2^5 - 2^4 = 32 - 16 = 16$$

This is correct since the sixteen odd numbers 1, 3, 5, ..., 27, 29, 31 are the only numbers less than 32 which are relatively prime to 32. All the other even numbers share the factor 2 with 2^5.

The three rules described are all that is needed to calculate $\phi(n)$ for any positive integer n once its factorisation is known.

Example: To calculate $\phi(9000)$, we first factorise 9000 to find that

$$9000 = 2^3 \times 3^2 \times 5^3$$

Then since 2^3, 3^2 and 5^3 are relatively prime to one another, we may write

$$\phi(9000) = \phi(2^3) \times \phi(3^2) \times \phi(5^3)$$

Since

$$\begin{aligned}
\phi(2^3) &= 2^3 - 2^2 = 8 - 4 = 4 \\
\phi(3^2) &= 3^2 - 3^1 = 9 - 3 = 6 \\
\phi(5^3) &= 5^3 - 5^2 = 125 - 25 = 20
\end{aligned}$$

it follows that

$$\phi(9000) = 4 \times 6 \times 100 = 2400$$

Perhaps you might like to verify this result directly.

In Code

The Euler–Femat Theorem (1736): If n is any natural number then

$$a^{\Phi(n)} \equiv 1 \,(\mathrm{mod}\, n)$$

for every natural number a satisfying $(a, n) = 1$.

Equivalently,

$$n \,|\, a^{\Phi(n)} - 1$$

for every natural number a satisfying $(a, n) = 1$.

Example: If $n = 18$, then $\phi(n) = \phi(18) = 6$. The six numbers less than 18 relatively prime to it are 1, 5, 7, 11, 13 and 17. Letting a be each of these numbers in turn, the Euler–Fermat theorem says that

$$
\begin{array}{lll}
1^6 \equiv 1\,(\mathrm{mod}\,18) & \text{or that} & 18\,|\,1^6 - 1 \\
5^6 \equiv 1\,(\mathrm{mod}\,18) & \text{or that} & 18\,|\,5^6 - 1 \\
7^6 \equiv 1\,(\mathrm{mod}\,18) & \text{or that} & 18\,|\,7^6 - 1 \\
11^6 \equiv 1\,(\mathrm{mod}\,18) & \text{or that} & 18\,|\,11^6 - 1 \\
13^6 \equiv 1\,(\mathrm{mod}\,18) & \text{or that} & 18\,|\,13^6 - 1 \\
17^6 \equiv 1\,(\mathrm{mod}\,18) & \text{or that} & 18\,|\,17^6 - 1 \\
\end{array}
$$

Checks:

$$
\begin{array}{ll}
1^6 - 1 = & 0 = 18 \times 0 \\
5^6 - 1 = & 15624 = 18 \times 868 \\
7^6 - 1 = & 117648 = 18 \times 6536 \\
11^6 - 1 = & 1771560 = 18 \times 98420 \\
13^6 - 1 = & 4826808 = 18 \times 268156 \\
17^6 - 1 = & 24137568 = 18 \times 1340976 \\
\end{array}
$$

When $n = p$ where p is a prime, $\phi(n) = \phi(p) = p - 1$. In this particular case, the Euler–Fermat theorem says that:

Appendix D – The Euler ϕ-function

If p is any prime number then

$$a^{p-1} \equiv 1 (\bmod p)$$

for every natural number a satisfying $(a, p) = 1$.

This is Fermat's little theorem (FLT) of 1640. Thus the Euler–Fermat theorem is a generalisation of the FLT to all natural numbers. A tremendous achievement!

Acknowledgements

We wish to thank Pat 'Herring' Ahern, Tom Barry, Kevin J. Kelly, Tom Laffey, Gerard Murphy and Denise O'Driscoll, who all read drafts of the manuscript. They generously devoted their holiday time to this duty, and we appreciate the many improvements of a mathematical and grammatical nature that they suggested.

Our particular thanks must go to Peter Carson of Profile Books. It was he who extended the invitation to write this book. We cursed him privately many times for so doing. The fates punished him for this great sin of making us an offer we couldn't, in conscience, refuse. He must have been forced many times to call on his reserves of patience and tact in order to encourage two amateurs in their struggle at pretending to be authors. He was forever helpful but never interfering, expending many hours in correspondence and reading with obvious care a number of drafts of different chapters. The fact that this book has seen the light of day owes much to his efforts. *Míle buíochas.*

A thousand thanks also to John Woodruff for his superb copyediting and the numerous improvements suggested by his knowledge of mathematical history. He has been a true champion of the reader. Thanks also to Kate Griffin and Andrew Franklin, both of Profile, for their wonderfully open ways and warm enthusiastic encouragement. A special thanks to Andrew's daughter, Miriam. Knowing that she enjoyed the puzzles and "couldn't wait to see the book", was an inspiration on the many occasions when our confidence was flagging.

In Code

Finally, we must commend Profile on the courage they have shown by publishing a book which contains as much mathematics as this one does. Only time will tell if they are as mad as we are in thinking that the general reading public is no longer intimidated by exposition which dares to contain technical detail.

Bibliography

Bell, E.T., *Men of Mathematics*, Simon & Schuster, New York, 1937.

Cipra, Barry, *What's Happening in the Mathematical Sciences*, Vol. 3, American Mathematical Society, Providence, RI, 1996.

Hardy, G.H., *A Mathematician's Apology*, Cambridge University Press, 1940.

Hoffman, Paul, *The Man Who Loved Only Numbers*, Fourth Estate, London, 1998.

Koestler, Arthur, *The Act of Creation*, Picador, London, 1964.

Roberts, Joe, *Lure of the Integers*, Mathematical Association of America, Washington, DC, 1992.

Singh, Simon, *Fermat's Last Theorem*, Fourth Estate, London 1997.

Singh, Simon, *The Code Book*, Fourth Estate, London, 1999.

Stoll, Clifford, *The Cuckoo's Egg*, Doubleday, London, 1989.

Young, Robert M., *Excursions in Calculus*, Mathematical Association of America, Washington, DC, 1993.

Index

A

Adelman, Leonard, 45, 119
Aer Lingus, 53
Ahern, Bertie, vii, 218
algorithms *see* names of
  individual algorithms
answers, 239–246

B

Baltimore Technologies, 170,
  179, 188, 216–218, 225, 227–229
Bell, Men of Mathematics, 180
Bell, E.T., 180
Bell Telephone Co., 161
Blarney, vii, 1, 2, 173, 201, 214,
  218
  Castle, 220
Box, G., 208
Burke, Rev. Thomas, 197

C

Caesar
  cipher, 55, 61, 68, 71, 72,
    74–76, 86, 149, 151, 192
  wheel, 70, 196

Caesar, Julius, 61, 69, 73, 75,
  192
Carmichael numbers, 102, 128
Cayley, Sir Arthur, 173, 188,
  225, 227
Cayley-Purser algorithm, 225,
  227
CBS News's *48 Hours*
  programme, 219
CESG *see* Communications-
  Electronics Security Group
chessboard squares, 134
Chinese remainder theorem,
  66, 182
ciphertext, 59
Cipra, Barry, 46
CIT, *see* Cork Institute of
  Technology
Clarkson, Ronald, 51
Cocks, Clifford, 161
Cole, Frank, 49
Communications-Electronics
  Security Group, 160
composite number, 31
congruence, 106, 107

Cork Institute of Technology (CIT), 2, 26, 181, 183, 184, 214, 220

D

Diffie, Whitfield, 147, 153, 160, 161, 185, 231
digraphs, 88
divide, 105
divisor, 29
Dylan, Bob, 2

E

Edison, Thomas, 210
Einstein, Albert, 56, 188, 208
Ellis, James, 160
Eratosthenes, sieve of, 38
Erdös, Paul, 33, 135
 The Man Who Loved Only Numbers, 135
Esat Telecom, vii, 53, 166, 198
Euclid, 42, 43, 95, 153, 248
 algorithm, 159, 160, 247–256
Euler, 44, 46, 119, 130, 134, 257, 260
 F-function, 257–261
 formula for generating primes, 46, 47
 number, 46, 47, 59
 prime, 47
Euler-Fermat theorem, 130, 155, 257–261
European Union Contest for Young Scientists, vii, 198, 229

F

Factorisation, 30
 complete, 34
 fast exponentiation algorithm, 125
Fermat
 formula for generating primes, 42, 46
 Last theorem, 118, 197
 Little Theorem, 57, 118–122, 126–130, 155, 160, 261
 number, 42, 43, 59
 prime, 43
Fermat, Pierre, 42, 43, 46, 59, 118, 124
Fitzpatrick, Patrick, 184
Flannery
 Brian, 199, 200, 211
 David, Jr., 9, 199, 211
 Eamonn, 199, 211, 236
 Michael, 2, 3, 57, 199, 200, 211
Folan, David, 198
Foley, Séan, vii, 52–54, 186, 187, 190, 194
Foley, Vincent, vii, 168, 190, 191, 195, 197, 201
functions, 95
 one-way, 136, 143
 trapdoor, 136, 145

G

Gardner, Martin, 46
Gates, Bill, 207
Gauss, Carl Friedrich, 28, 52, 106, 108, 181

Index

GCHQ *see* Government Communications Headquarters
golden ratio (f), 130
googol, 112
Gorenstein, Daniel, 234
Göttingen University, 181
Government Communications Headquarters (GCHQ), 160
Great Internet Mersenne Prime Search, 51
Guardian, 204
Guy, R, 63

H
Hajratwala, Nayan, 51
Hardy, G.H., 132
  A Mathematician's Apology, 132
Hellman, Martin, 147, 153, 160, 161, 185
Hilbert
  numbers, 35
  primes, 35
Hilbert, David, 144
Hill, Lester, S., 180, 183, 184
Howley, Karina, 197
Hurley, Hugh, 191, 198
Hurley, Raphael, 168, 191, 197

I
Imbush, Frank, 195
integers, 103
Intel, vii, 169–170, 186–188, 197
International Science and Engineering Fair (ISEF), 169

International Standard Book Number (ISBN), 116
Irish Times, 5, 193, 199
ISBN *see* International Standard Book Number
IT@Cork, 202
Ivory, James, 119

J
Jackson, Samuel, 6
Jacobi, Carl Gustav Jacob, 180
Jenkins, G., 208
Jones, J.P., 51

K
Kalmann filter, 208
Kaufmann, Stephen, 190
Kerckhoff, Auguste, 75, 100
Koestler, Arthur, 13, 14
  The Act of Creation, 13

L
Lanczos, C., 208
Landry, F., 45
Legendre, Adrien-Marie, 52
Lehmer, D. N., 50
Lucas, Édouard, 50

M
magic squares, 16
Mathematica, 50, 54, 57, 58, 73, 168, 172, 184, 190, 213
matrices, 173–177
megaprime, 51
Merkle, Ralph, 147, 161

Mersenne
  number, 47, 49, 51, 59
  prime, 48, 51
Mersenne, Fr. Marin, 44, 46–51
Microsoft, 167
modulo, 72
modulus (mod), 63
monographic substitution
  cipher, 69
Monty's game show, 135

N

names of individual algorithms
  Cayley Purser, 225, 227
  Euclid algorithm, 159, 160,
    247–256
natural logarithms, base of (e),
  130
natural number, 24
Newton, Sir Isaac, 132, 208
Nobel Prize ceremonies, 232
non-communicative
  multiplication, 172
number field sieve, 208
numerical equivalents, 71

O

one-way, 136, 143
O'Neill, Eoin, 193–196

P

Patent Office, 197
pi (π), decimal expansion of,
  134
plaintext, 59
Pollard, H., 208

Pomerance, Carl, 37
PowerPoint, 167, 222–225
primality, 102
prime decomposition, 35
prime number, 31, 33
prime number theorem, 52, 160
probability, 134
product, 30
proof, 42
pseudoprimes, 126
public key cryptography, 148
Purser, Michael, 171–173, 178,
  179, 186, 188, 189, 203, 204,
  208, 216, 217, 225–229
  *Introduction to Error-
    Correcting Codes*, 188
puzzles, 6–16
  solutions, 236–238
Pythagoras, 5, 131

R

RDS, vii, 53, 191, 193
relatively prime, 85
remote coin-tossing protocol,
  137, 139, 141
residue class, 104
Rivest, Ronald, 45, 119, 185,
  205, 233
Roberts, Joe, 63
  Lure of the Integers, 63
RSA129, 46
RSA, vii, 46, 55, 56, 119, 153,
  155–157, 159, 160, 164, 178,
  179, 184, 189, 190, 193, 205,
  230
rule of nines, 115

Index

S

Sato, D., 51
Scientific American, 46, 153
Scoil Mhurie gan Smál, 1
Scott, Tony, 197
Shamir, Adi, 45, 119, 164, 185
Singh, Simon, 42, 118, 160, 197
   Fermat's Last Theorem, 42
   The Code Book, 160
square, symmetries of, 23
Stoll, Clifford, 144, 145
   The Cuckoo's Egg, 144
Supple, B., 191, 196

T

Theory of general relativity, 208
Thessaloniki, vii, 198, 231
threshold schemes, 163
Times, viii, 51, 202, 204, 206,
   214, 226
trial division algorithm, 37
Trinity College, 172

U

unique factorisation theorem, 35

University College Cork,
   (UCC), 169, 184

V

Vandyck, Michel, 183
Von Neumann, John, 13

W

Wada, H., 51
Whyte, William, 171–173,
   188, 189, 203, 204, 218,
   225–230
Wiens, H., 51
Williamson, Malcolm, 161
Willis, Bruce, 6
Woltman, George, 51

Y

Young, Robert, M., 27
   Excursions in Calculus,
   27

Z

Zero-knowledge protocol,
   162